Developing Num
NUMBERS AND :...
NUMBER SYSTEM

ACTIVITIES FOR THE DAILY MATHS LESSON

year

6

Hilary Koll and Steve Mills

A & C BLACK

Contents

Reprinted 2000, 2002
Published 2000 by A&C Black Publishers Limited
37 Soho Square, London W1D 3QZ
www.acblack.com

ISBN O-7136-5236-5

Copyright text © Hilary Koll and Steve Mills, 2000
Copyright illustrations © Gaynor Berry, 2000
Copyright cover illustration © Charlotte Hard, 2000

The authors and publisher would like to thank the following teachers for their advice in producing this series of books:
Tracy Adam; Shilpa Bharambe; Hardip Channa; Sue Hall; Ann Hart; Lydia Hunt; Madeleine Madden; Helen Mason;
Anne Norbury; Jane Siddons; Judith Wells; Fleur Whatley.

A CIP catalogue record for this book is available from the British Library.

A & C Black uses paper produced with elemental chlorine-free pulp, harvested from managed sustainable forests.

Printed in Great Britain by St Edmundsbury Press Ltd, Bury St Edmunds, Suffolk.

Introduction

Developing Numeracy: Numbers and the Number System is a series of seven photocopiable activity books designe to be used during the daily maths lesson. The books focus on the first strand of the National Numeracy Strateg *Framework for teaching mathematics*. The activities are intended to be used during the time allocated to pur activities; they aim to reinforce the teaching within the lesson and provide practice and consolidation of th objectives contained in the framework document.

Year 6 supports the teaching of mathematics to Year 6 children by providing a series of activities to develop ar reinforce essential skills in number work. The activities relate to place value, ordering and rounding; properties numbers and number sequences; and fractions, decimals, percentages, ratio and proportion. They build on th children's understanding of the concepts taught in Year 5 and also introduce –

- multiplying and dividing decimals mentally by 10 or 100, and integers by 1000;
- finding the difference between a positive and a negative integer, or two negative integers;
- recognising prime numbers to at least 20;
- reducing a fraction to its simplest form;
- rounding decimals to the nearest tenth.

Extension

Many of the activity sheets end with a challenge (**Now try this!**) which reinforces and extends the childrer learning, and provides the teacher with the opportunity for assessment. Where children are asked to carry out a activity the instructions are clear to enable them to work independently, although the teacher may wish to rea out the instructions and provide further support where necessary. The children may need to write their answe on a separate piece of paper.

Organisation

For some of the activities it will be useful to have available coloured pencils, counters, scissors, number lin (including negative numbers), place value cards (sometimes called arrow cards) and 100-squares. To help teache to select appropriate learning experiences for their children, the activities are grouped into sections within ea book. The pages are not intended to be presented in the order in which they appear unless otherwise stated.

Teachers' notes

Very brief notes are provided at the end of most pages, giving ideas and suggestions for maximising th effectiveness of the activity sheets. These notes could be masked before photocopying.

Structure of the daily maths lesson

The recommended structure of the daily maths lesson for Key Stage 2 is as follows:

Start to lesson, oral work, mental calculation	5–10 minutes
Main teaching and pupil activities	about 40 minutes
Plenary	about 10 minutes

Each lesson should include:
- a pacey start with the whole class involved in counting, oral and mental calculation work;
- some direct interactive teaching of the whole class on the maths objective for the day;
- group or individual activities linked to the objective of the lesson. The teacher should focus on one grou to continue teaching directly. The activities in the **Developing Numeracy** books are designed to be carried out in the time allocated to group activities;
- a plenary with the whole class after the group activities are ended to consolidate and extend the children's learning through questions and discussion.

The following chart shows an example of the way in which an activity from this book can be used to achieve the required organisation of the daily maths lesson for Year 6 children.

Percentage path (page 62)

Start to the lesson Begin by asking the children to find one tenth of a variety of numbers, for example: *"What is one tenth of 20... 400... 330?"* Practise finding one half and one quarter of numbers (finding one quarter by halving and halving again). Ask the children to describe how they would find three quarters of a number (for example, by finding one quarter and multiplying by three, or by finding one quarter and subtracting it from the original number). Find three quarters of 20, 400 and 88 using a range of strategies.	**5–10 minutes**

Main teaching and pupil activities Draw a line on the board and mark the half-way point. Ask the children to describe one half in different ways, for example, $\frac{1}{2}$, 0.5 or 50%. Write 1 and 100% at the right-hand end of the line.	**about 40 minutes**

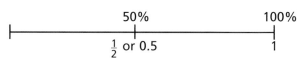

Discuss the different ways of describing one quarter and three quarters and mark them on the line. Show the different ways of describing one tenth, two tenths and so on in the same way. Remove the numbers from the line and write a different value, such as 80 m, at the right-hand end.

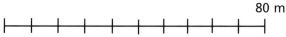

Ask the children to find one tenth or ten per cent of 80 m and write this at the appropriate mark. Ask them to find twenty per cent, thirty per cent and so on until they see a pattern. Give the children the **Percentage path** sheet (page 62, **Developing Numeracy: Numbers and the Number System Year 6**). Ask them to follow the path, working out the percentages mentally. (They could draw number lines to help them if necessary.) More able children could also be given a page from a catalogue and asked to find the new price if each item cost eighty per cent of the original price.

Plenary Discuss the children's answers and go over a few examples on the board. Ask the children to explain how they calculated each answer and discuss how this might have been done if they had been given a calculator to work with. What would they have keyed in? Show an example (such as 60% of £14) which could be found by keying in 60 ÷ 100 x 14. Encourage the children to practise learning the halves of numbers by heart and remind them of strategies for finding one quarter and one half.	**about 10 minutes**

Further activities

The following activities provide some practical ideas for whole class mental and oral work. These are intended to introduce or reinforce the main teaching part of the lesson.

Place value, ordering and rounding

Show me place value
Each child has a set of place value cards (sometimes called arrow cards). Play 'show me' activities where each child shows a number by holding cards in the air as you say, *"Show me 63... how many tens and how many ones? Show me the number between 69 and 71,"* and so on. You could extend this activity to cover rounding and finding the difference, by saying: *"Show me 86 rounded to the nearest ten,"* or *"Show me the difference between 24 and 37."*

Totals

Draw a 'dartboard' as shown. Ask the children to imagine they have three darts, then set them challenges such as: "*What is the closest score you can make to 68, 245, 1029? How many different scores between 800 and 900 can you make? What is the highest odd number you can make?*"

Properties of numbers and number sequences

Show me

Each child has a set of digit cards from 0 to 9. Play 'show me' activities where each child shows a number by holding one or two digit cards in the air as you say, "*Show me a multiple of 6 between 31 and 39... a multiple of 8... the highest prime number under 100 you can make with two cards.*"

Spot the pattern

Using a 100-square, ask the children to circle and find the total of any three numbers in a line, for example 21, 22, 23. What do they notice? (The totals will all be multiples of 3.) Ask children to find three numbers in a line with a total of 66, 93, and so on.

Jumping along

Ask the children to count on or back from a given starting number, for example, backwards in steps of 1.2 fro 5.7 or forwards in quarters from $2\frac{1}{2}$. This game can be played in small groups or around the whole class.

Fractions, decimals, percentages, ratio and proportion

Counting stick

Use a stick which is divided into ten equal sections, such as a metre stick with each 10 cm coloured. Hold the sti so that all the children can see it and point to each section along the stick in turn. Decide on a whole numb decimal or fraction (for example, $8\frac{1}{2}$ or 2.5) and ask the children to count in steps of that size as you point to ea section. This provides practice in counting forwards and backwards and helps the children to remember t multiples of a given number. It also provides reinforcement of fraction and decimal work, allowing the children form a better visual picture of the numbers and their relationships to each other.

People numbers

Invite ten children to stand facing the class and give each of them a card with a fraction or decimal on it, whi they hold in front of them. Ask them to order themselves from highest to lowest. Then invite individual childr from the rest of the class to change places with those at the front, for example: "*Jo, change places with 4.67.*"

Numbers in the environment

Discuss with the children examples of numbers that they can see and hear around them which exemplify t number work they are doing, for example, percentage discounts in sales, decimal prices, larger numbers such lottery prizes, and features in magazines or newspapers which show probability recorded as decimals or fractio

---

Selected answers

p 9

2. eight hundred and twenty-four thousand
3. four hundred and seventy thousand, two hundred and seventy
4. six million, three hundred and forty
5. eight million, seven hundred and five thousand and ten
6. one million, sixty thousand and ninety
7. thirty nine thousand, one hundred
8. six hundred and twenty thousand, five hundred
9. five million and ninety thousand
10. four million, six hundred
11. three million, three hundred and three thousand, three hundred

p 11

1. 23000
2. 235000
3. 250000
4. 2350000
5. 2300000
6. 2500000
7. 253000
8. 25000
9. 25310000
10. 23511000
11. 2351000
12. 2531000

p 12

2. £2630.20
3. £2340.70   4. £6148.70
5. £4506.10   6. £78113.20
7. £8154.20   8. £4938.20
9. £10961.40 10. £719.30
11. £3751.90 12. £154200.30

13. £7140   14. £263.02
15. £234.07   16. £614.87
17. £450.61   18. £7811.32

Now try this!
1. £41320   2. £909090
3. £33333   4. £191900

p 13
1. 62, 6.2, 0.62
2. 87, 8.7, 0.87
3. 5.5, 0.55, 0.055

4. 12.7, 1.27, 0.127
5. 483.2, 48.32, 4.832
6. 6799.1, 679.91, 67.991

Now try this!
1. 472   2. 370   3. 10063

p 15
Now try this!
2. 50.2 ÷ 100
3. 0.52 ÷ 100   4. 2.5 ÷ 100

p 16
2. 100 times smaller
3. 100 times smaller
4. 1000 times larger
5. 1000 times smaller
6. 100 times smaller
7. 1000 times larger
8. 100 times larger

w try this!
1000 times larger
10 times larger
100 times larger

7
w try this!
rgest number: 42700
aallest number: 0.427

19
7100
180000
36500
2015
400
–10
12600
0.05

20
9000, 8900, 8910
6000, 6000, 6010
7000, 7500, 7500
16000, 16400, 16430
23000, 22700, 22680
60000, 59800, 59820
61000, 61400, 61400
50000, 49900, 49910
86000, 85500, 85550

21
1. 5°C 2. 9°C
3. 4°C 4. 1°C
5. 2°C 6. 15°C
7. 3°C 8. 14°C
9. 9°C 10. 24°C
11. 15°C 12. 16°C
13. 11°C 14. 14°C
15. 18°C 16. 29°C
17. 23°C 18. 17°C
19. 14°C 20. 20°C

w try this!
°C

22
–32, –30, –29, –17, 0, 6, 14
–15, –14, –9, –2, 7, 16, 22
–62, –38, –21, –19, 2, 5, 35
–99, –42, –27, 1, 16, 27, 50, 100
–65, –27, –21, –19, –3, 3, 16, 25
–77, –50, –19, –18, –15, 6, 43, 47, 50
–90, –43, –32, –16, –14, –12, 10, 25, 70

23
unting back in 11s
1, 190, 179, 168, 157, 146, 5, 124, 113, 102, 91

unting back in 15s
0, 185, 170, 155, 140, 125, 0, 95, 80, 65, 50

Counting back in 19s
199, 180, 161, 142, 123, 104, 85, 66, 47, 28, 9

Counting back in 21s
201, 180, 159, 138, 117, 96, 75, 54, 33, 12, –9

Counting back in 25s
200, 175, 150, 125, 100, 75, 50, 25, 0, –25, –50

Now try this!
Counting on in 11s
–50, –39, –28, –17, –6, 5, 16, 27, 38, 49

Counting on in 19s
–100, **–81,** –62, –43, –24, –5, 14, 33, 52, 71

p 24
Counting on in steps of 15
5, 20, 35, 50, 65, 80, 95,
11, 26, 41, 56, 71, 86, 101
17, 32, 47, 62, 77, 92, 107
23, 38, 53, 68, 83, 98, 113
29, 44, 59, 74, 89, 104, 119
35, 50, 65, 80, 95, 110
41, 56, 71, 86, 101
47, 62, 77, 92
53, 68, 83
59, 74

Counting back in steps of 19
329, 310
337, 318, 299
345, 326, 307, 288
353, 334, 315, 296, 277
361, 342, 323, 304, 285, 266
369, 350, 331, 312, 293, 274, 255
358, 339, 320, 301, 282, 263, 244
347, 328, 309, 290, 271, 252, 233
336, 317, 298, 279, 260, 241, 222
325, 306, 287, 268, 249, 230, 211

p 25
Now try this!
• 7.0
• 14.0

p 26
Counting on in steps of 0·5
0, 0·5, 1, 1·5, 2, 2·5, 3, 3·5,
4, 4·5, 5, 5·5, 6, 6·5, 7, 7·5,
8, 8·5, 9, 9·5, 10, 10·5, 11,
11·5, 12, 12·5, 13, 13·5

Counting on in steps of 0·25
1·11, 1·36, 1·61, 1·86, 2·11,
2·36, 2·61, 2·86, 3·11, 3·36,
3·61, 3·86, 4·11, **4·36,** 4·61,
4·86, 5·11, 5·36, 5·61, 5·86,
6·11, 6·36, 6·61, 6·86, 7·11,
7·36, 7·61

p 27
1. 8, 1, –6, –13, decreasing by 7
2. –88, –113, decreasing by 25
3. 25, 36, 49, pattern of square numbers
4. 21, 28, increasing by 2, 3, 4, 5, 6, 7…
5. 110, 121, 132, increasing by 11
6. 78, 108, increasing by 5, 10, 15, 20…
7. –58, –72, decreasing by 14

Now try this!
1, 1, 2, 3, 5, 8, 13, 21, 34, 55, 89, 144, 233

p 28
1. even
2. even
3. odd
4. even
5. even
6. even
7. even

Now try this!
1. even 2. even
3. odd 4. even

p 29
Now try this!
Prime numbers from 0–50:
2, 3, 5, 7, 11, 13, 17, 19, 23, 29, 31, 37, 41, 43, 47

p 30
1. 42, 63, 56
2. 64, 48, 56
3. 36, 54, 18, 72
4. 36, 63, 81, 72, 54
5. These are all multiples of 2 except for 3.
6. These are all multiples of 3 except for 16.
7. These are all multiples of 3 and 6 except for 14.

p 31
1. true 2. false 3. false
4. false 5. true
6. true 7. false 8. true
9. false 10. false 11. true

Now try this!
• 84
• 56
• 18

p 33
1. 343
2. 247
3. 6255
4. 296
5. 527
6. 211

p 34
2. 9 cm 3. 5 cm
4. 11 cm 5. 7 cm 6. 8 cm
7. 4 cm 8. 10 cm 9. 12 cm

Now try this!
1. 17 cm
2. 24 cm
3. 27 cm
4. 46 cm
• 6084 cm^2

p 35
Prime numbers uncoloured:
2, 3, 5, 7, 11, 13, 17, 19, 23, 29, 31, 37, 41, 43, 47, 53, 59, 61, 67, 71, 73, 79, 83, 89, 97

p 36
1. 1 x 36, 2 x 18, 3 x 12, 4 x 9, 6 x 6
2. 1 x 72, 2 x 36, 3 x 24, 4 x 18, 6 x 12, 8 x 9
3. 1 x 64, 2 x 32, 4 x 16, 8 x 8
4. 1 x 100, 2 x 50, 4 x 25, 5 x 20, 10 x 10

Now try this!
• 21

p 37
2. 2 x 2 x 5 3. 2 x 2 x 2 x 5
4. 2 x 2 x 2 x 2 5. 2 x 3 x 3
6. 2 x 2 x 3 x 3 7. 2 x 2 x 2 x 3

p 38
2. $3\frac{3}{5}$ 3. $5\frac{2}{5}$
4. $3\frac{1}{5}$ 5. $12\frac{1}{3}$ 6. $3\frac{1}{6}$
7. $7\frac{1}{6}$ 8. $7\frac{3}{8}$ 9. $9\frac{2}{7}$
10. $10\frac{5}{8}$ 11. $9\frac{3}{4}$ 12. $9\frac{8}{9}$
13. $\frac{43}{7}$ 14. $\frac{28}{3}$ 15. $\frac{33}{8}$
16. $\frac{43}{8}$ 17. $\frac{58}{9}$ 18. $\frac{29}{5}$
19. $\frac{79}{10}$ 20. $\frac{59}{7}$ 21. $\frac{27}{4}$
22. $\frac{47}{6}$ 23. $\frac{27}{7}$ 24. $\frac{80}{9}$

Now try this!
• $13\frac{2}{6}$, $13\frac{1}{3}$, $\frac{40}{3}$

p 41
2. $\frac{35}{40} > \frac{32}{40}$
3. $\frac{27}{36} < \frac{28}{36}$
4. $\frac{16}{24} > \frac{15}{24}$
5. $\frac{20}{24} > \frac{18}{24}$
6. $\frac{36}{45} < \frac{40}{45}$
7. $\frac{63}{90} > \frac{60}{90}$
8. $\frac{21}{56} < \frac{24}{56}$
9. $\frac{42}{70} > \frac{40}{70}$
10. $\frac{56}{63} > \frac{54}{63}$
11. $\frac{32}{40} > \frac{30}{40}$
12. $\frac{20}{90} < \frac{27}{90}$

Now try this!
$\frac{6}{30}$, $\frac{9}{30}$, $\frac{15}{30}$, $\frac{25}{30}$, $\frac{27}{30}$

p 42
Now try this!
1. < 2. >
3. < 4. >

p 44
1. 21, 18, 6, 60, 27, 120
2. 20, 44, 36, 24, 80, 240
3. 14, 28, 35, 70, 42, 49
4. 28, 36, 24, 80, 120

Now try this!
2. 40 cm
3. 7 cm   4. 4 g
5. 17 g   6. 100 g

p 45
1. $\frac{3}{100}$
2. $\frac{17}{100}$
3. $\frac{3}{10}$ or equivalent
4. $\frac{1}{2}$ or equivalent
5. $1\frac{1}{2}$ or equivalent
6. $1\frac{1}{5}$ or equivalent
7. $2\frac{1}{20}$ or equivalent
8. $3\frac{19}{100}$ or equivalent
9. $\frac{4}{100}$ or equivalent
10. $\frac{12}{100}$ or equivalent
11. $\frac{9}{10}$ or equivalent
12. $\frac{1}{4}$ or equivalent
13. $1\frac{99}{100}$ or equivalent
14. $4\frac{3}{10}$ or equivalent
15. $6\frac{12}{100}$ or equivalent
16. $\frac{1}{1000}$
17. $\frac{19}{1000}$
18. $\frac{47}{1000}$
19. $\frac{129}{1000}$
20. $\frac{543}{1000}$
21. $\frac{798}{1000}$
22. $1\frac{822}{1000}$ or equivalent
23. $4\frac{761}{1000}$ or equivalent
24. $\frac{1}{1000}$
25. $\frac{49}{1000}$
26. $\frac{225}{1000}$ or equivalent
27. $\frac{999}{1000}$
28. $1\frac{284}{1000}$ or equivalent
29. $3\frac{562}{1000}$ or equivalent

Now try this!
1. $\frac{1}{12}$
2. $\frac{1}{52}$ or $\frac{7}{365}$
3. $\frac{1}{365}$

p 47
1. 8   2. 24
3. 24   4. 32
5. 3   6. 5
7. 2   8. 6
9. 8   10. 16
11. 28   12. 56
13. 18   14. 21
15. 9   16. 24

Now try this!
1. 10
2. 6
3. 5
4. 27
5. 4
6. 18

p 48
Now try this!
2. 37·42
3. 33·71   4. 26·41
5. 90·98   6. 100·06
7. 8·72   8. 1·06
9. 0·95   10. 30·03

p 49
1. 0·07
2. 0·4
3. 10
4. 0·006
5. 0·8
6. 6·321
7. 90·802
8. 12·057
9. 100·006

Now try this!
1. $\frac{6}{100}$ 2. $\frac{2}{1000}$
3. $\frac{1}{10}$ 4. $\frac{9}{1000}$

p 50
2. −0·01
3. +0·1   4. −0·02
5. −0·001   6. +0·01
7. −0·2   8. +0·01

Now try this!
1. x 10   2. x 100
3. ÷1000   4. ÷100

p 51
1. 0·25m   2. 0·49m   3. 1·86m
4. 0·3m   5. 0·9m   6. 0·04m
7. 0·125kg   8. 0·44kg   9. 0·3kg
10. 0·625l   11. 0·22l   12. 0·1l
13. 1615g   14. 5520g   15. 400g
16. 182ml   17. 6450ml   18. 6200ml

Now try this!
1. 1·95kg   2. 5·8l
3. 1·6m   4. 2·893kg

p 53
1. 6·2, 6·36, 6·89, 6·98, 16·4
2. 1·575, 1·6, 1·625, 1·65, 1·7
3. 7·867, 7·886, 8·785, 8·865, 8·875
4. 4·0, 4·16, 4·67, 4·76, 14·2
5. 5·5, 5·57, 5·575, 5·6, 5·66

p 54
1. 17·78 m, 17·5 m, 7·75 m, 7·7 m, 7·557 m
2. 10·8 kg, 1·81 kg, 1·8 kg, 1·08 kg, 1·008 kg, 0·8 kg
3. 6·6 l, 6·222 l, 6·22 l, 6·2 l, 6·02 l, 0·6 l
4. 90·9 kg, 9·99 kg, 9·9 kg, 9·4 kg, 9·099 kg, 9·09 kg
5. 12·7 l, 2·7 l, 1·27 l, 1·2 l, 1·027 l, 0·127 l

p 55
2. 8, 8·5
3. 7, 7·3
4. 6, 5·8
5. 15, 14·8
6. 22, 22·4
7. 128, 127·6
8. 636, 636·2
9. 522, 522·2
10. 369, 368·5
11. 892, 891·6
12. 425, 425·0
13. 330, 330·0
15. 8·1
16. 7·5   17. 6·5
18. 1·0   19. 6·0

p 56
6. $6\cdot2 \sim \frac{620}{100}$
2. $1\cdot25 \sim \frac{125}{100}$ 7. $0\cdot62 \sim \frac{62}{100}$
3. $0\cdot02 \sim \frac{2}{100}$ 8. $6\cdot02 \sim \frac{602}{100}$
4. $0\cdot2 \sim \frac{20}{100}$ 9. $6\cdot6 \sim \frac{660}{100}$
5. $1\cdot2 \sim \frac{120}{100}$ 10. $0\cdot66 \sim \frac{66}{100}$
12. $\frac{3}{100}$
13. $\frac{15}{10}$ or equivalent
14. $\frac{427}{100}$ or equivalent
15. $\frac{111}{1000}$
16. $\frac{723}{1000}$
17. $\frac{616}{1000}$
18. $\frac{1472}{1000}$ or equivalent
19. 0·42
20. 0·87
21. 0·04
22. 1·2

Now try this!
fractions equivalent to 1·5:
$\frac{150}{100}$, $1\frac{1}{2}$, $1\frac{5}{10}$, $\frac{15}{10}$

p 57
1. 0·125   2. 0·33333
3. 0·375   4. 0·66666
5. 0·75   6. 0·11111
7. 0·8   8. 0·22222
9. 0·875   10. 0·55555
11. 0·35   12. 0·77777
13. <   14. <   15. >
16. <   17. >   18. >

Now try this!
1. 0·3333333   2. 0·6666666
3. 1·3333333   4. 1·6666666

p 59
2. 47%   3. 25%   4. 41%
5. 20%   6. 16%   7. 14%   8. 15%
1. 72   72%
2. 51   51%
3. 88   88%

Now try this!
1. 21%
2. 79%

p 60
2. $34\% = \frac{34}{100} = 0\cdot34$
3. $92\% = \frac{92}{100} = 0\cdot92$
4. $6\% = \frac{6}{100} = 0\cdot06$
5. $30\% = \frac{30}{100} = 0\cdot3$
6. $5\% = \frac{5}{100} = 0\cdot05$

Now try this!
2. $\frac{23}{25}$
3. $\frac{29}{50}$ 4. $\frac{17}{50}$
5. $\frac{1}{25}$ 6. $\frac{1}{20}$

p 61
2. 75   3. 100
4. 95   5. 65   6. 135
7. 450   8. 225   9. 300
10. 285   11. 195   12. 405
13. 3   14. 90   15. 12
16. 11   17. 70   18. 8
19. 24   20. 720   21. 96
22. 88   23. 560   24. 64
25. 54   26. 72   27. 270
28. 810   29. 360   30. 99

p 62
£75, £2.40, 12 m,
28 kg, 9l, £54, 6 kg,
1·8 cm, 140 m, 48 kg,
13 cm, £300, 4 m,
£5, £9, 20 km, 162 kg,
56 m, 7·14l, 2·3 g, 36 m,
12 m, 1 kg, 4·5l, 1l

p 63
1. £96   2. £54.40   3. £37.
4. £20   5. £10   6. £3.
7. £97.50   8. £52.50   9. £37
10. £19.50   11. £10.05   12. £4

p 64
2. 52%   3. 76%
4. 60%   5. 58%   6. 81%
7. 84%   8. 69%   9. 53%
10. 58% 11. 91% 12. 25%

Now try this!
$\frac{14}{55}$, $\frac{13}{25}$, $\frac{48}{90}$, $\frac{37}{64}$, $\frac{46}{80}$, $\frac{24}{?}$
$\frac{45}{65}$, $\frac{12}{16}$, $\frac{38}{50}$, $\frac{13}{16}$, $\frac{27}{32}$, $\frac{64}{?}$

Great times

- **Multiply the numbers in the columns by** 10 **or by** 100 .
- **Write the answers in words.**

	M	Hth	Tth	Th	H	T	U		
1.				4	6	3	0	x 10 =	Forty-six thousand, three hundred
2.			8	2	4	0	0	x 10 =	
3.			4	7	0	2	7	x 10 =	
4.		6	0	0	0	3	4	x 10 =	
5.		8	7	0	5	0	1	x 10 =	
6.		1	0	0	6	0	9	x 10 =	

	M	Hth	Tth	Th	H	T	U		
7.				3	9	1		x 100 =	
8.				6	2	0	5	x 100 =	
9.			5	0	9	0	0	x 100 =	
10.			4	0	0	0	6	x 100 =	
11.			3	3	0	3	3	x 100 =	

- **Use the digits** 6 , 2 , 0 , 8 **and** 1 **to make six** five-digit numbers .
- **Multiply each number by** 100 .
- **Write the answers in words.**

Teachers' note Discuss with the children how the digits move across the columns when numbers are multiplied by 10 and 100. Some children may need to write the number in figures before writing it in words.

Developing Numeracy
Numbers and the Number System
Year 6
© A & C Black 2000

10 and 100 times larger

- **Cut out the cards.**
- **Put the** 10 **and** 100 **cards in a row face down.**
- **Put the rest of the number cards in a pile face down.**
- **Take one card from the row and one from the pile and multiply the two numbers together.**
- **Write down the question and write the answer in figures, then words.**
- **Return the** 10 **or** 100 **card to the row.**
- **Repeat until the pile is used up.**

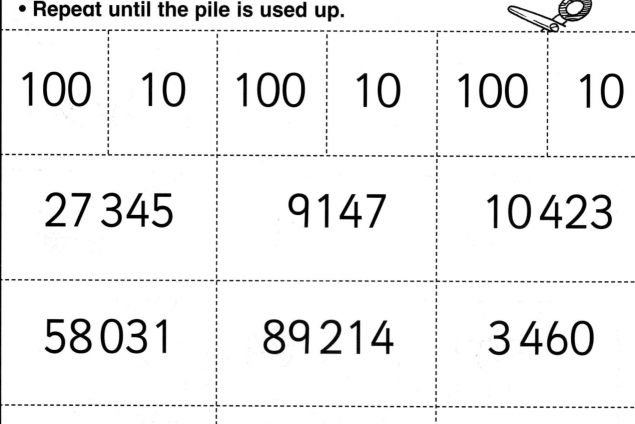

100	10	100	10	100	10
27 345		9147		10 423	
58 031		89 214		3 460	
1907		6189		6 713	
35 650		71 040		4 729	

Teachers' note To increase their mental agility, the children could play the game against the clock, allowing themselves five seconds to answer each question. They could also make their own cards to add to the game. To use this activity without cutting out the cards, the children could multiply each number by 10 and then by 100.

Developing Numeracy
Numbers and the Number Syste
Year 6
© A & C Black 2000

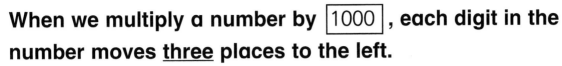

Move over!

When we multiply a number by $\boxed{1000}$, each digit in the number moves <u>three</u> places to the left.

Hth	Tth	Th	H	T	U
			4	1	7

$\boxed{\text{x 1000}}$ =

Hth	Tth	Th	H	T	U
		4	1	7	0	0	0

• Match each number in the column to a number that

is $\boxed{1000 \text{ times larger}}$.

Multiply each number in the column by 1000.

2 300 000

1. 23

2. 235

350 000

235 000

3. 250

23 000

4. 2350

253 000

5. 2300

250 000

2 500 000

6. 2500

25 000

7. 253

8. 25

2 531 000

2 351 000

9. 25 310

23 511 000

23 510 000

10. 23 511

11. 2351

2 350 000

12. 2531

25 310 000

25 000 000

• **Write the numbers to the left of the column in words.**

Example:

2 300 000 = two million, three hundred thousand

Developing Numeracy
Numbers and the Number System
Year 6
© A & C Black 2000

Lottery winners

- **Divide each jackpot between** ten **winners.**
- **Write how much each winner receives.**

1. £714 000   £ _71 400_

2. £26 302   £ _____

3. £23 407   £ _____

4. £61 487   £ _____

5. £45 061   £ _____

6. £781 132   £ _____

7. £81 542   £ _____

8. £49 382   £ _____

9. £109 614   £ _____

10. £7 193   £ _____

11. £37 519   £ _____

12. £1 542 003   £ _____

- **Divide each of these jackpots between** 100 **winners.**
- **Write how much each winner receives.**

13. £ 714 000   £ _____

14. £ 26 302   £ _____

15. £ 23 407   £ _____

16. £ 61 487   £ _____

17. £ 45 061   £ _____

18. £ 781 132   £ _____

In four different lottery draws, 100 **winners each received these amounts.**

1. £413.20   2. £9 090.90

3. £333.33   4. £1 919

- **What were the total jackpots?**

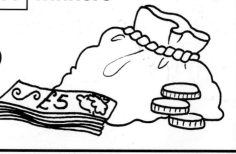

Teachers' note Remind the children that they should write decimals with two decimal places in the context of money, for example, £1.20, not £1.2.

Developing Numeracy
Numbers and the Number Syste[m]
Year 6
© A & C Black 2000

Dividing paths

• **Divide the number in each house by** $\boxed{10}$, $\boxed{100}$ **and** $\boxed{1000}$.

1.

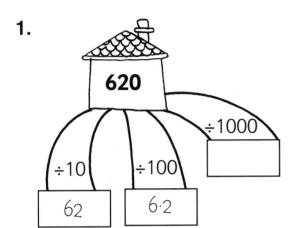

620

÷1000

÷10 → 62

÷100 → 6·2

2.

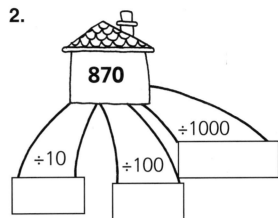

870

÷1000

÷10

÷100

3.

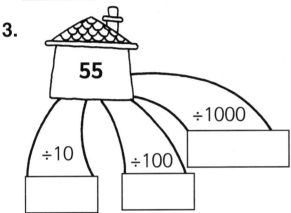

55

÷1000

÷10

÷100

4.

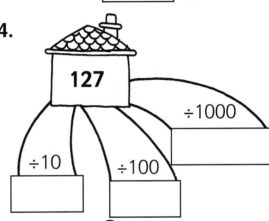

127

÷1000

÷10

÷100

5.

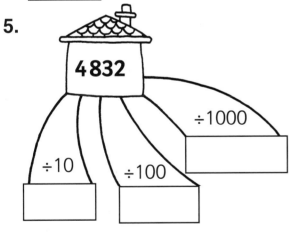

4 832

÷1000

÷10

÷100

6.

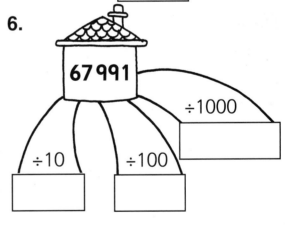

67 991

÷1000

÷10

÷100

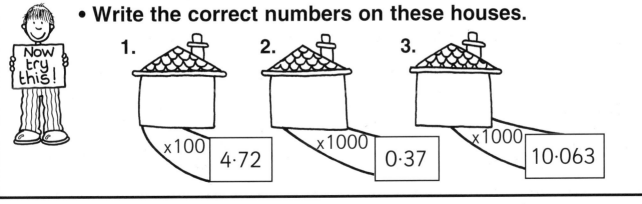

• **Write the correct numbers on these houses.**

1. ×100 → 4·72

2. ×1000 → 0·37

3. ×1000 → 10·063

Teachers' note To introduce the activity, explain with examples that division is the inverse of multiplication. In the extension activity, the children need to use division to work out what number leads to the number at the end of the path.

Developing Numeracy
Numbers and the Number System
Year 6
© A & C Black 2000

13

Decimal multiplication

- **Cut out the cards and put them in a pile face down.**
- **Pick a card and time how quickly you can work out the answer mentally. Then write down your answer.**
- **Do the same for each card.**

Check your answers on a calculator.

0·17 x 10	3·56 x 100	21·4 x 10
13·04 x 100	9·71 x 10	14·26 x 100
10·01 x 10	31·34 x 100	18·09 x 10
30·08 x 100	4·19 x 10	25·94 x 100
53·51 x 10	1·81 x 100	0·253 x 10
11·41 x 100	18·014 x 10	3·147 x 100

Teachers' note The children could complete the questions on paper to see the movement of digits across place value columns. This game could also be played without cutting out the cards; the children could work through the calculations one by one. They should check their answers on a calculator at the end.

Developing Numeracy
Numbers and the Number Syst
Year 6
© A & C Black 2000

Decimal division

These cards have been arranged to make a question.

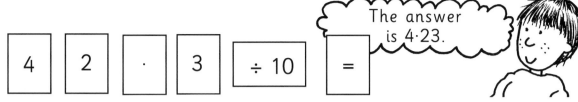

The answer is 4·23.

| 4 | 2 | · | 3 | ÷ 10 | = |

• **Arrange the numbers on the cards to make questions.**

Write the questions and answers.

| 6 | 2 | 4 | · | ÷ 10 | = |

1. $24·6 ÷ 10 = 2·46$ 2. _____

3. _____   4. _____

5. _____   6. _____

| 1 | 0 | · | 8 | ÷ 100 | = |

7. _____   8. _____

9. _____   10. _____

11. _____   12. _____

Now try this!

• **Arrange the numbers on these cards to make a question for each answer.**

| ÷ 100 | 5 | 0 | · | 2 |

1. $2·05 ÷ 100$ = 0·0205   2. _____ = 0·502

3. _____ = 0·0052   4. _____ = 0·025

Teachers' note This activity could be introduced by giving the children digit cards and a decimal point card and asking them to make similar questions at the front of the class.

Developing Numeracy
Numbers and the Number System
Year 6
© A & C Black 2000

Number bugs

- **Look at these pairs of numbers. How many times larger or smaller is the first number than the second number?**

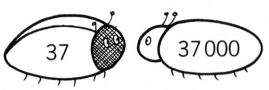

1. _1000 times smaller_

2. _____

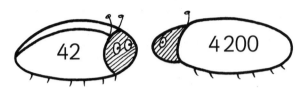

3. _____

4. _____

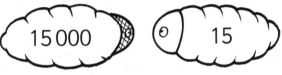

5. _____

6. _____

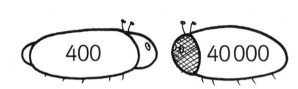

7. _____

8. _____

Now try this!

- **How many times larger is the whole number than the decimal?**

1. _100 times larger_

2. _____

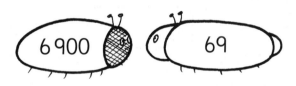

3. _____

4. _____

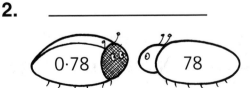

Teachers' note As an additional extension activity, the children could write ten decimals and multiply each by 1000.

Developing Numeracy
Numbers and the Number Syst⁕
Year 6
© A & C Black 2000

Trailfinder

- **Choose a trail and follow the arrows from start to finish.**
- **Write the answers in the boxes on the way.**
- **When you reach the finish, go back to the start and try a different trail.**

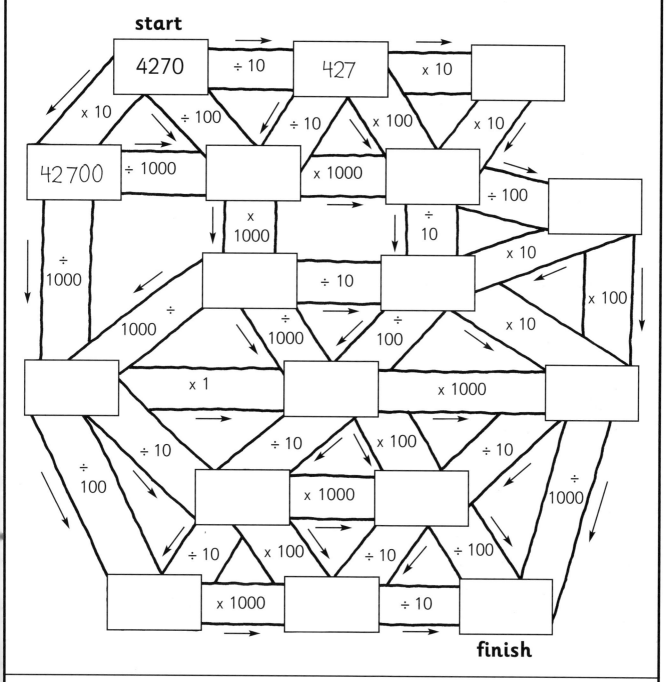

start

| 4270 | ÷ 10 | 427 | x 10 | |

x 10   ÷ 100   ÷ 10   x 100   x 10

| 42 700 | ÷ 1000 | | x 1000 | | ÷ 100 | |

÷ 1000

x 1000   ÷ 10   x 10

÷ 1000   ÷ 10   x 10   x 100

÷ 1000   ÷ 1000   ÷ 100   x 10

x 1   x 1000

÷ 100   ÷ 10   ÷ 10   x 100   ÷ 10   ÷ 1000

x 1000

÷ 10   x 100   ÷ 10   ÷ 100

x 1000   ÷ 10

finish

- **Which is the largest number on this page?** _____
- **Which is the smallest number on this page?** _____

Teachers' note The answer in the 'finish' box should be the same whichever route the children have taken.

**Developing Numeracy
Numbers and the Number System
Year 6
© A & C Black 2000**

Estimation challenge

-  **Estimate** **the answers to these questions.**
- **Write notes to explain how you would check to see how close your estimates are.**

1. How many 10p coins would make a straight line 100 m long? ☐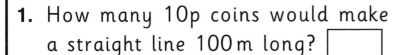

_____

2. How many books are there in the school library? ☐

_____

3. How many bricks are there in the school hall? ☐

_____

4. How many times does your heart beat in a month? ☐

_____

5. How many times do you blink in one hour? ☐

_____

- **Set three estimation challenges for a partner.**
- **Work out your own estimate for each.**
- **How close are your estimates to your partner's?**
- **Did you work them out in the same way?**

Teachers' note If no bricks are visible in the school hall, you could suggest an alternative wall for the children to estimate the number of bricks. Model with the children how they can use multiplication techniques to improve their estimates. Encourage them to show their working. The children could be allowed to use calculators for this activity.

Developing Numeracy
Numbers and the Number System
Year 6
© A & C Black 2000

Line them up

- Estimate the numbers that the arrows are pointing to.

1. 10 000 — [10 600] ↓ — 11 000

2. [ ] ↓ 7 000 — 7 500

3. 100 000 — [ ] ↓ 200 000

4. 36 000 — [ ] ↓ 37 000

5. [ ] ↓ 2 000 — 2 100

6. 0 — [ ] ↓ 1 000

7. −50 — [ ] ↓ 0

8. 12 000 — [ ] ↓ 14 000

9. [ ] ↓ 0 — 1

- **Draw five more number lines for a friend to try.**
- **Write down your answers before your friend tries them.**

Teachers' note During the extension activity, the children should make make a note of the numbers they think are indicated by the arrows on their number lines, so that they can compare and discuss their estimates with their friend.

**Developing Numeracy
Numbers and the Number System
Year 6
© A & C Black 2000**

Football fans

Here are the attendance figures for ten football matches.

• Round each figure to the nearest 1000 , 100 and 10 .

	attendance	to nearest 1000	to nearest 100	to nearest 10
1.	4721	5000	4700	4720
2.	8909			
3.	6005			
4.	7499			
5.	16426			
6.	22677			
7.	59818			
8.	61400			
9.	49909			
10.	85545			

Now try this!

• **Would you estimate these numbers to the nearest**
10 , 100 , 1000 , 10000 , 100000 **or** 1000000 ?

the number of	to the nearest
1. people in Britain	
2. words in a dictionary	
3. beans in a can	
4. tiles on a roof	
5. windows in a tower block	
6. children in a class	

• **Compare and discuss your answers with a partner.**

Teachers' note For the extension activity, ensure that children understand that they do not have to make the estimates, but must specify how it would be most sensibly rounded. They should also understand there is not one 'correct' answer to each question.

Developing Numeracy
Numbers and the Number Syste
Year 6
© A & C Black 2000

Spot the difference

- **Find the difference between the temperatures in each pair.**

 Use the thermometer to help you.

difference **difference**

1. −2°C, 3°C [ ]   2. 5°C, −4°C [ ]

3. −7°C, −3°C [ ]   4. −6°C, −7°C [ ]

5. −4°C, −2°C [ ]   6. 8°C, −7°C [ ]

7. −6°C, −9°C [ ]   8. −15°C, −1°C [ ]

9. −8°C, 1°C [ ]   10. −14°C, 10°C [ ]

11. 0°C, −15°C [ ]   12. −8°C, 8°C [ ]

13. −13°C, −2°C [ ]   14. −6°C, 8°C [ ]

15. −9°C, 9°C [ ]   16. −15°C, 14°C [ ]

17. −12°C, 11°C [ ]   18. −2°C, 15°C [ ]

19. −1°C, −15°C [ ]   20. −7°C, 13°C [ ]

°C
15 14 13 12 11 10 9 8 7 6 5 4 3 2 1 0 −1 −2 −3 −4 −5 −6 −7 −8 −9 −10 −11 −12 −13 −14 −15

Now try this!

- **Follow the number chain on the chart.**

  What was the temperature on Friday? _____

Sunday	Monday	Tuesday	Wednesday	Thursday	Friday
3°C	dropped by 5°C	rose by 1°C	fell by 7°C	decreased by 2°C	increased by 1°C

Teachers' note Try to discourage children from following such rules as 'add the numbers and ignore the minus sign' to find differences. This does not work when finding the difference between two negative numbers.

Developing Numeracy
Numbers and the Number System
Year 6
© A & C Black 2000

21

From smallest to biggest

• **Write these integers in order, starting with the smallest.**

1.

    -32 -30 -29

    ~~-32~~ 14 -17 6 ~~-29~~ ~~-30~~ 0

2.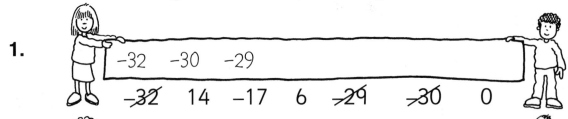

    -15 7 22 -14 16 -9 -2

3.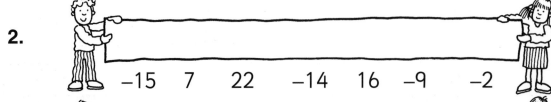

    -38 5 -62 -19 -21 35 2

4.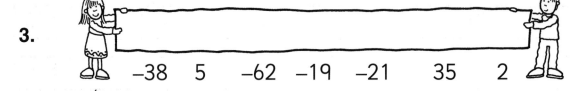

    100 -99 27 -27 16 -42 50 1

5.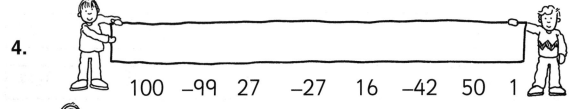

    3 -65 -27 -3 -19 16 25 -21

6.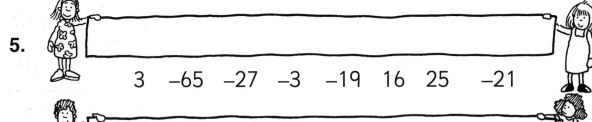

    47 -18 -77 43 6 -15 -19 -50 50

7.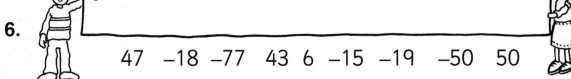

    10 -16 -12 -43 -90 70 25 -32 -14

• **Write eight pairs of negative integers with**

a | difference of 18 | .

| **Example:** -20, -2 |

Teachers' note If the children need additional help to complete the extension activity, encourage them to draw a number line.

Developing Numeracy
Numbers and the Number System
Year 6
© A & C Black 2000

Take a step back

• **Join the numbers as you count back. Use a different colour each time.**

start	start	start	start	start
count back in 11s	count back in 15s	count back in 19s	count back in 21s	count back in 25s
201	200	199	201	200
185	190	180	175	195
159	170	179	161	150	155
128	138	155	168	142	125
116	117	157	140	100	123
147	146	96	75	125	104
135	136	50	75	85	110
76	124	66	25	54	95
113	47	0	70	80	33
28	−25	102	2	12	65
−50	9	−10	−9	91	50

Now try this!

• **Count on in steps of** 11 **to complete the sequence.**

| −50 | −39 | | | | | | | |

• **Count on in steps of** 19 **to complete the sequence.**

| −100 | −81 | | | | | | | |

Teachers' note The children should practise counting aloud forwards and backwards past zero before they tackle this activity.

Developing Numeracy
Numbers and the Number System
Year 6
© A & C Black 2000

Upstairs, downstairs

- **Write the missing numbers on the staircase. Count on in steps of** $\boxed{15}$ **.**

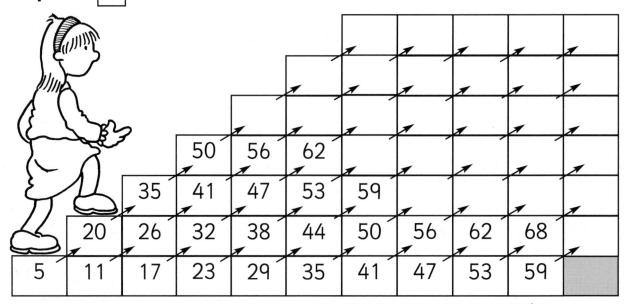

5	11	17	23	29	35	41	47	53	59	
20	26	32	38	44	50	56	62	68	
35	41	47	53	59	
50	56	62	

- **Write the missing numbers on this staircase.**
  Count back in steps of $\boxed{19}$ **.**

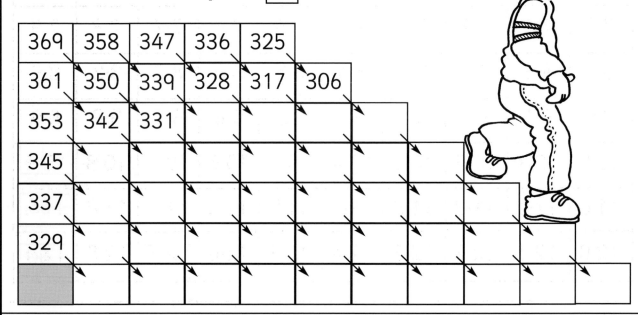

369	358	347	336	325
361	350	339	328	317	306
353	342	331
345
337
329

Now try this!

- **Look at the horizontal rows of numbers in the first staircase. Can you find a pattern?**
- **Now look for a pattern in the horizontal rows of the second staircase.**

Teachers' note Encourage the children to subtract 20 and add 1 when they are counting back in steps of 19.

Developing Numeracy
Numbers and the Number Sys
Year 6
© A & C Black 2000

Stepping out

- **Count in steps of** $\boxed{0 \cdot 2}$. **Colour them yellow.**
- **Count in steps of** $\boxed{0 \cdot 5}$. **Colour them orange.**
- **Count in steps of** $\boxed{0 \cdot 7}$. **Colour them blue.**

start	0·1	0·2	0·3	0·4	0·5	0·6	0·7	0·8	0·9
1·0	1·1	1·2	1·3	1·4	1·5	1·6	1·7	1·8	1·9
2·0	2·1	2·2	2·3	2·4	2·5	2·6	2·7	2·8	2·9
3·0	3·1	3·2	3·3	3·4	3·5	3·6	3·7	3·8	3·9
4·0	4·1	4·2	4·3	4·4	4·5	4·6	4·7	4·8	4·9
5·0	5·1	5·2	5·3	5·4	5·5	5·6	5·7	5·8	5·9
6·0	6·1	6·2	6·3	6·4	6·5	6·6	6·7	6·8	6·9
7·0	7·1	7·2	7·3	7·4	7·5	7·6	7·7	7·8	7·9
8·0	8·1	8·2	8·3	8·4	8·5	8·6	8·7	8·8	8·9
9·0	9·1	9·2	9·3	9·4	9·5	9·6	9·7	9·8	9·9
10·0	10·1	10·2	10·3	10·4	10·5	10·6	10·7	10·8	10·9
11·0	11·1	11·2	11·3	11·4	11·5	11·6	11·7	11·8	11·9
12·0	12·1	12·2	12·3	12·4	12·5	12·6	12·7	12·8	12·9

- **Describe the pattern that each colour makes.**
- **Which number is coloured in all three colours?** _____
- **If the pattern continued, what would be the next number coloured in all three colours?** _____

Teachers' note Before the children tackle this activity, tell them that, in the finished grid, some squares will be coloured in more than one colour.

Developing Numeracy
Numbers and the Number System
Year 6
© A & C Black 2000

Starry sky

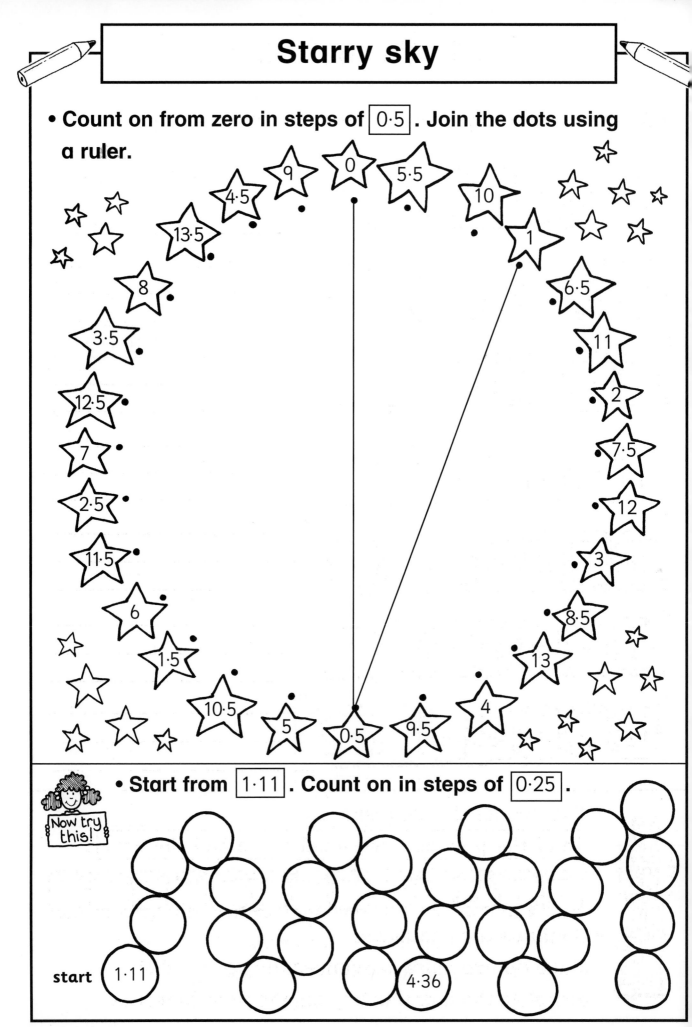

- **Count on from zero in steps of** $\boxed{0.5}$ **. Join the dots using a ruler.**

Stars with numbers: 0, 9, 5·5, 4·5, 10, 13·5, 1, 8, 6·5, 3·5, 11, 12·5, 2, 7, 7·5, 2·5, 12, 11·5, 3, 6, 8·5, 1·5, 13, 10·5, 5, 0·5, 9·5, 4

- **Start from** $\boxed{1.11}$ **. Count on in steps of** $\boxed{0.25}$ **.**

Now try this!

start (1·11)   (4·36)

Teachers' note The children could use a calculator to check their answers.

Developing Numeracy
Numbers and the Number System
Year 6
© A & C Black 2000

What's the rule?

- **Continue each sequence. Explain the rule in words.**

1.  29 22 15

1. _____
_____
_____

2. 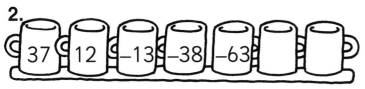 37 12 −13 −38 −63

2. _____
_____
_____

3. 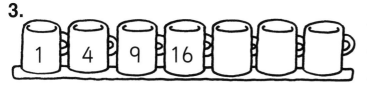 1 4 9 16

3. _____
_____
_____

4.  1 3 6 10 15

4. _____
_____
_____

5.  66 77 88 99

5. _____
_____
_____

6.  3 8 18 33 53

6. _____
_____
_____

7. 12 −2 −16 −30 −44

7. _____
_____
_____

- **The rule for this sequence is**

| add the previous two numbers to find the next | .

 1 1 2 3 5

- **Continue the sequence.**

- **Make up two more sequences. Ask a friend to complete them and to explain the rules in words.**

Teachers' note The number pattern in the extension activity is called the *Fibonacci sequence*.

Developing Numeracy
Numbers and the Number System
Year 6
© A & C Black 2000

27

Odds and evens

- Write ⬚odd⬚ or ⬚even⬚ to make a correct statement.
- Give three examples to prove each statement.

1. even + even = ⬚even⬚   6 + 2 = 8

        22 + 18 = 40   1120 + 2430 = 3550

2. even x even = ⬚ ⬚ _____

_____

3. odd x odd = ⬚ ⬚ _____

_____

4. even x odd = ⬚ ⬚ _____

_____

5. even x odd x even = ⬚ ⬚ _____

_____

6. even x odd x odd = ⬚ ⬚ _____

_____

7. even x even x odd x odd = ⬚ ⬚ _____

_____

Now try this!

- **Predict whether the answers to these questions will be ⬚odd⬚ or ⬚even⬚ .**

1. 674 x 12 x 101 ⬚ ⬚   **2.** 650 x 13 x 49 ⬚ ⬚

3. 1035 x 5 x 17 ⬚ ⬚   **4.** 42 x 16 x 12 x 48 ⬚ ⬚

- **Check your predictions using a calculator.**

Teachers' note Make sure the children appreciate that more than one example must be provided to prove a general statement.

Developing Numeracy
Numbers and the Number System
Year 6
© A & C Black 2000

Match the multiples

The top line of the left-hand chart shows that ⎡48⎤ is a
⎡multiple of 1, 2, 4, 6 and 8⎤ .

- **Complete the charts.**

		multiple of									
		1	2	3	4	5	6	7	8	9	10
1.	48	✓	✓		✓		✓		✓		
2.	14										
3.	16										
4.	24										
5.	27										
6.	36										
7.	90										
8.	56										
9.	28										
10.	35										
11.	72										
12.	32										
13.	54										

		multiple of									
		1	2	3	4	5	6	7	8	9	10
14.	49										
15.	38										
16.	81										
17.	60										
18.	63										
19.	42										
20.	64										
21.	18										
22.	30										
24.	21										
24.	88										
25.	80										
26.	66										

A ⎡prime number⎤ **is a number which is only
a multiple of** ⎡1⎤ **and itself.**

- **Colour the prime numbers.**

15	17	21	23	25	29

- **List all the prime numbers from** ⎡0⎤ **to** ⎡50⎤ **.**

Teachers' note Note that one is not a prime number as it only has one factor. Two is the only
even prime number.

Developing Numeracy
Numbers and the Number System
Year 6
© A & C Black 2000

Multiple choice

1. Circle the multiples of 7 **.**

42　47　63　57　17　41　56　54

2. Circle the multiples of 8 **.**

63　64　49　36　48　54　28　81　56

3. Circle the multiples of 6 **.**

21　36　54　32　45　57　64　18　72

4. Circle the multiples of 9 **.**

36　21　28　35　63　81　72　17　56　54

• **Write the correct numbers to complete these statements.**

5.　18　30　24　12　14　6　3　10　16　8　4

These are all multiples of ＿＿ except for ＿＿ .

6.　30　24　18　12　15　6　16　9　27　21　3

These are all multiples of ＿＿ except for ＿＿ .

7.　24　12　14　18　36　30　6　54　42　60　48

These are all multiples of ＿＿＿＿＿＿ except for ＿＿ .

• **Write three numbers that are** common multiples **of** 2, 4, 5 and 10 **. Example:** 100

• **Write three numbers that are** common multiples **of** 2, 5, 6 and 10 **. Example:** 30

Teachers' note Introduce the children to the term 'common multiple' – a number that is a multiple of more than one number (apart from one and itself) – for example, 36 is a multiple of 2, 3, 6, 9, 12 and 18.

**Developing Numeracy
Numbers and the Number Syst
Year 6
© A & C Black 2000**

True or false banners

• Which banners are true ✔ and which are false ✘ ?

1. 16 is a common multiple of 2 and 8. ☐

2. 12 is a common multiple of 2 and 5. ☐

3. The smallest common multiple of 5 and 6 is 60. ☐

4. 5, 10 and 15 are common multiples of 2 and 5. ☐

5. The smallest common multiple of 6 and 8 is 48. ☐

6. 18, 36 and 54 are common multiples of 3 and 6. ☐

7. 63 is a common multiple of 9 and 6. ☐

8. The smallest common multiple of 7 and 6 is 42. ☐

9. 96 is the smallest common multiple of 8 and 12. ☐

10. 72 and 64 are common multiples of 8 and 9. ☐

11. 42 is a common multiple of 2, 3, 6, 7 and 14. ☐

Now try this!

• **What is the smallest common multiple of** [7 and 12] **?** ☐

• **What is the smallest common multiple of** [8 and 14] **?** ☐

• **What is the smallest common multiple of** [9 and 18] **?** ☐

Teachers' note To test the banner statements, encourage the children to write out <u>all</u> the multiples of each number first.

Developing Numeracy
Numbers and the Number System
Year 6
© A & C Black 2000

Exactly divisible

- **Colour yellow the numbers that are** exactly divisible by 8 .
- **Colour blue the numbers that are** exactly divisible by 3 .

Halve and halve again. If the answer is even, the original number is a multiple of 8.

If the sum of a number's digits is divisible by 3, the number is a multiple of 3.

30					129	165	84	147	9
63	152	32	88		162	80	16	304	27
87	51	114	141		111		171		90
	40		36		93		3	104	54
12	81	105	6		126		78		138
135			56		45	112	108	21	69
132	273	64			60	57	136	405	
66			400	800	156	117	15		
18	123	42	99	150				102	
160				75	39	33	153	159	320

Now try this!

- **Write five numbers that are** exactly divisible by 3 and 8 . ___ ___ ___ ___ ___
- **Write five numbers that are** exactly divisible by 5 and 8 . ___ ___ ___ ___ ___
- **Write two numbers that are** exactly divisible by 3, 5 and 8 . ___ ___

Teachers' note If the squares are coloured correctly, a blue trail will be made around the grid and the yellow squares will form symmetrical patterns.

Developing Numeracy
Numbers and the Number Sys
Year 6
© A & C Black 2000

Key questions

• In each key, one of the numbers is not exactly divisible by the number in the lock. Circle the odd one out.

1.
   9 | 216   810   351   981   343

2. 6 | 144   210   342   247   636
    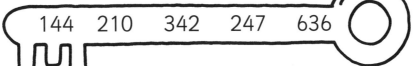

3. 25 | 600   150   6255   84525   75

4. 3 | 636   267   960   888   296

5. 8 | 760   192   527   360   1136
    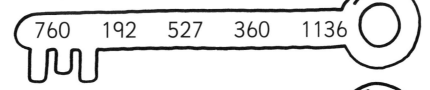

6. 7 | 77   140   4900   211   280
    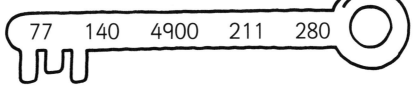

Now try this!

• **True or false? Give examples to prove your answers.**

1. A number that is exactly divisible by 9 is also exactly divisible by 3. _____   _____

2. A number that is exactly divisible by 6 is also exactly divisible by 3. _____   _____

• **Write three more true or false division statements.**

• **Give them to a friend to test.**

Teachers' note In the extension activity, ensure that the children realise that more than one example is needed to prove a statement.

Developing Numeracy
Numbers and the Number System
Year 6
© A & C Black 2000

Square areas

- **Find the length of the sides of these squares.**

They are not drawn to scale.

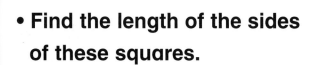

1.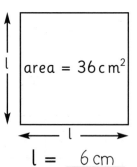

area = 36 cm²

l

l

$l = \underline{6\ cm}$

2.

area = 81 cm²

$l = \underline{\hspace{2cm}}$

3.

area = 25 cm²

$l = \underline{\hspace{2cm}}$

4.

area = 121 cm²

$l = \underline{\hspace{2cm}}$

5.

area = 49 cm²

$l = \underline{\hspace{2cm}}$

6.

area = 64 cm²

$l = \underline{\hspace{2cm}}$

7.

area = 16 cm²

$l = \underline{\hspace{2cm}}$

8.

area = 100 cm²

$l = \underline{\hspace{2cm}}$

9.

area = 144 cm²

$l = \underline{\hspace{2cm}}$

Now try this!

- **Find the length of the sides of these squares.**

Use a calculator.

1.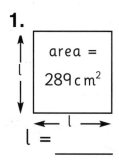

area = 289 cm²

l

l

$l = \underline{\hspace{2cm}}$

2.

area = 576 cm²

$l = \underline{\hspace{2cm}}$

3.

area = 729 cm²

$l = \underline{\hspace{2cm}}$

4.

area = 2116 cm²

$l = \underline{\hspace{2cm}}$

- **The sides of a square are** 78 cm **in length. What is the area?** _____

Teachers' note Remind the children that the area of a rectangle can be found by multiplying the length by the breadth. Show children how to use the square root key on a calculator.

**Developing Numeracy
Numbers and the Number Syst**
Year 6
© A & C Black 2000

Prime examples

- **Follow the instructions and colour each square you land on.**
- **Do not colour the starting squares.**

Use the same colour for each instruction.

1. Start on 2. Count in twos.
2. Start on 3. Count in threes.
3. Start on 4. Count in fours.
4. Start on 5. Count in fives.
5. Start on 6. Count in sixes.
6. Start on 7. Count in sevens.
7. Start on 8. Count in eights.
8. Start on 9. Count in nines.
9. Start on 10. Count in tens.

1	2	3	4	5	6	7	8	9	10
11	12	13	14	15	16	17	18	19	20
21	22	23	24	25	26	27	28	29	30
31	32	33	34	35	36	37	38	39	40
41	42	43	44	45	46	47	48	49	50
51	52	53	54	55	56	57	58	59	60
61	62	63	64	65	66	67	68	69	70
71	72	73	74	75	76	77	78	79	80
81	82	83	84	85	86	87	88	89	90
91	92	93	94	95	96	97	98	99	100

- **You should have 25 numbers left uncoloured. Write them here.**

___ ___ ___ ___ ___

___ ___ ___ ___ ___

___ ___ ___ ___ ___

- **What are these numbers called?** _____

Now try this!

- **Choose eight numbers from your list.**
- **Write all the factors of each number. Example:**
- **What do you notice?**

```
      13
     /  \
    1    13
```

Teachers' note Explain to the children that one is not considered to be a prime number as it only has one factor. Prime numbers have two factors.

Developing Numeracy
Numbers and the Number System
Year 6
© A & C Black 2000

Factor trees

• **Write on the leaves all the** $\boxed{pairs\ of\ factors}$ **for the number on the tree trunk. Draw as many extra leaves as you need.**

1.

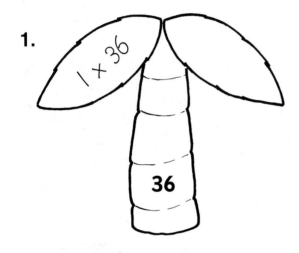

1 x 36

36

2.

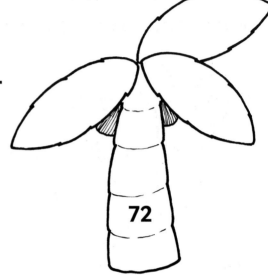

72

3.

64

4.

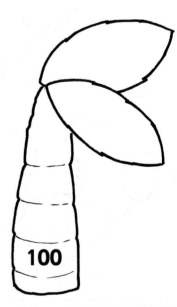

100

Now try this!

• **Circle all the** $\boxed{prime\ numbers}$ **on the factor trees.**
• **The factors of a number are** $\boxed{1}$**,**$\boxed{3}$**,**$\boxed{7}$ **and** $\boxed{21}$**. What is the number? ____**
• **Draw factor trees for the numbers** $\boxed{56}$ **,** $\boxed{63}$ **,** $\boxed{81}$ **,** $\boxed{96}$**.**

Teachers' note Explain that the numbers in the first extension activity can be called prime factors, that is, they are factors that are also prime numbers.

**Developing Numeracy
Numbers and the Number Sys**
Year 6
© A & C Black 2000

Factor eyes

The ⬚prime factors of 12 are 2, 2 and 3 because ⬚2 x 2 x 3 = 12 and ⬚2 and 3 are prime numbers.

- **Read the number on the alien's body.**
- **Write on the aliens' eyes the prime factors of the number.**

Remember, one is <u>not</u> a prime number.

- **Multiply some or all of these ⬚prime factors to make ten numbers between 1 and 100.**

| 2 | 2 | 5 | 3 | 3 | 7 |

Examples: 2 x 2 x 7 = 28   2 x 5 x 7 = 70

Developing Numeracy
Numbers and the Number System
Year 6
© A & C Black 2000

Fraction action

- **Write these** | improper fractions | **as** | mixed numbers | .

1. $\frac{15}{7}$ = $2\frac{1}{7}$ 2. $\frac{18}{5}$ = ☐   3. $\frac{27}{5}$ = ☐

4. $\frac{32}{10}$ = ☐   5. $\frac{37}{3}$ = ☐   6. $\frac{19}{6}$ = ☐

7. $\frac{43}{6}$ = ☐   8. $\frac{59}{8}$ = ☐   9. $\frac{65}{7}$ = ☐

10. $\frac{85}{8}$ = ☐   11. $\frac{39}{4}$ = ☐   12. $\frac{89}{9}$ = ☐

- **Write these** | mixed numbers | **as** | improper fractions | .

13. $6\frac{1}{7}$ = ☐   14. $9\frac{1}{3}$ = ☐   15. $4\frac{1}{8}$ = ☐

16. $5\frac{3}{8}$ = ☐   17. $6\frac{4}{9}$ = ☐   18. $5\frac{4}{5}$ = ☐

19. $7\frac{9}{10}$ = ☐   20. $8\frac{3}{7}$ = ☐   21. $6\frac{3}{4}$ = ☐

22. $7\frac{5}{6}$ = ☐   23. $3\frac{6}{7}$ = ☐   24. $8\frac{8}{9}$ = ☐

- **Circle the mixed numbers and fractions that are equivalent to** $\frac{80}{6}$ **.**

$13\frac{2}{6}$ $12\frac{2}{6}$ $13\frac{1}{3}$ $\frac{40}{3}$

- **Write three mixed numbers or fractions that are equivalent to** $\frac{42}{10}$ **.** _____

Teachers' note Remind the children that improper fractions are 'top-heavy', that is, the numerator is greater than the denominator.

Developing Numeracy
Numbers and the Number Sy
Year 6
© A & C Black 2000

Equivalent fractions

- Sort the fractions into groups of equivalent fractions .
- Write each group on a different raindrop.

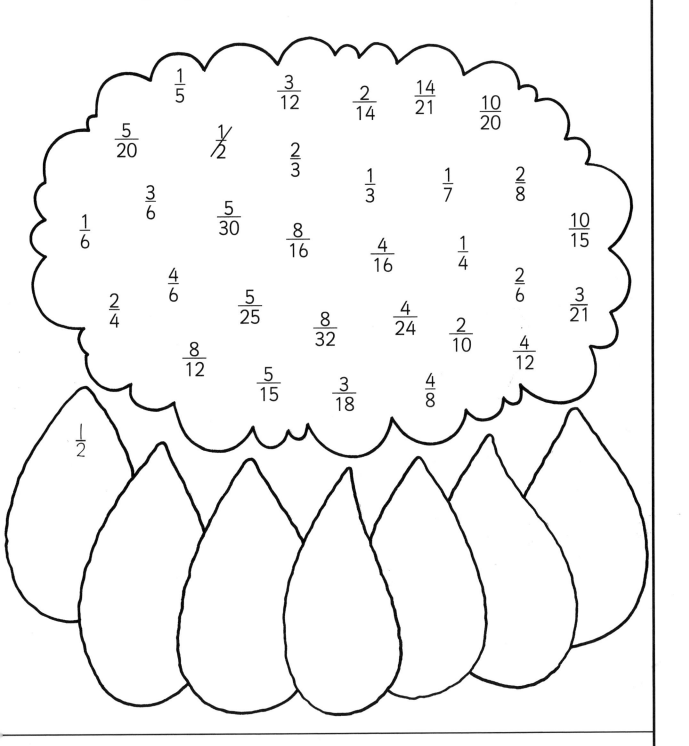

$\frac{1}{5}$ $\frac{3}{12}$ $\frac{2}{14}$ $\frac{14}{21}$ $\frac{10}{20}$

$\frac{5}{20}$ $\frac{1}{2}$ $\frac{2}{3}$

$\frac{1}{3}$ $\frac{1}{7}$ $\frac{2}{8}$

$\frac{3}{6}$ $\frac{5}{30}$

$\frac{1}{6}$ $\frac{8}{16}$ $\frac{1}{4}$ $\frac{10}{15}$

$\frac{4}{16}$

$\frac{4}{6}$ $\frac{2}{6}$ $\frac{3}{21}$

$\frac{2}{4}$ $\frac{5}{25}$ $\frac{8}{32}$ $\frac{4}{24}$ $\frac{2}{10}$ $\frac{4}{12}$

$\frac{8}{12}$ $\frac{5}{15}$ $\frac{3}{18}$ $\frac{4}{8}$

$\frac{1}{2}$

- Write two new equivalent fractions on each raindrop. Write them in a different colour.

Now try this!

Teachers' note Remind the children that equivalent fractions are worth the same, that is, they have the same value.

Developing Numeracy
Numbers and the Number System
Year 6
© A & C Black 2000

39

Machine magic

- **Follow the instructions on the machines to create equivalent fractions.**

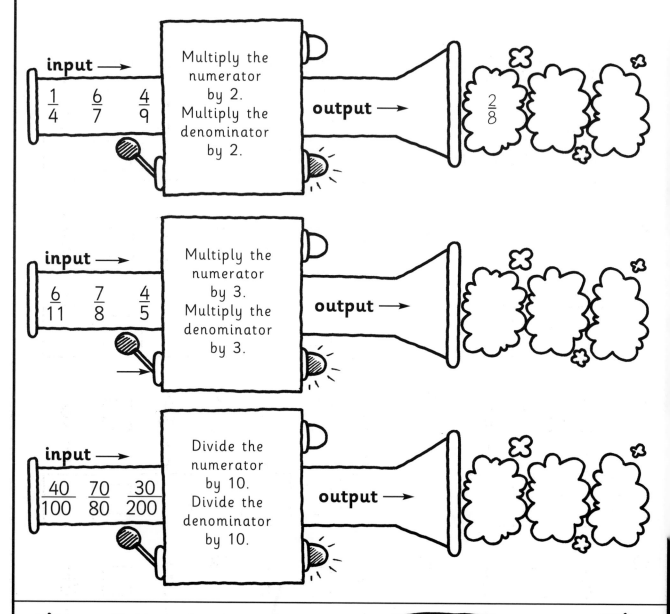

input ⟶

$\frac{1}{4}$ $\frac{6}{7}$ $\frac{4}{9}$

Multiply the numerator by 2. Multiply the denominator by 2.

output ⟶

$\frac{2}{8}$

input ⟶

$\frac{6}{11}$ $\frac{7}{8}$ $\frac{4}{5}$

Multiply the numerator by 3. Multiply the denominator by 3.

output ⟶

input ⟶

$\frac{40}{100}$ $\frac{70}{80}$ $\frac{30}{200}$

Divide the numerator by 10. Divide the denominator by 10.

output ⟶

Now try this!

- **Follow the instruction on the cog to create equivalent fractions.**

Multiply or divide the numerator <u>and</u> the denominator.

input ÷5 output	input ÷3 output	input x4 output	input x7 output
$\frac{5}{15}$ $\frac{1}{3}$	$\frac{6}{9}$	$\frac{1}{7}$	$\frac{5}{6}$
$\frac{25}{30}$	$\frac{18}{33}$	$\frac{3}{5}$	$\frac{6}{7}$

Teachers' note Emphasise to the children that multiplying or dividing the numerator and denominator by the same number will create equivalent fractions.

Developing Numeracy
Numbers and the Number Sys
Year 6
© A & C Black 2000

Common denominators

- Rewrite each pair of fractions using a | common denominator |.
- Use | > | or | < | to show which fraction is larger.

1. $\frac{4}{10}$ | > | $\frac{3}{8}$

$\frac{16}{40}$ | > | $\frac{15}{40}$

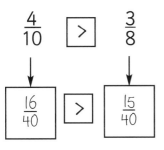

2. $\frac{7}{8}$ | | $\frac{4}{5}$

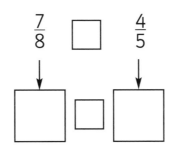

3. $\frac{3}{4}$ | | $\frac{7}{9}$

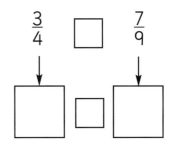

4. $\frac{2}{3}$ | | $\frac{5}{8}$

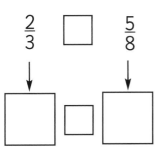

5. $\frac{5}{6}$ | | $\frac{6}{8}$

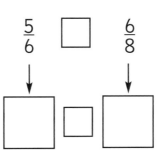

6. $\frac{4}{5}$ | | $\frac{8}{9}$

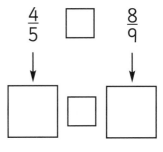

7. $\frac{7}{10}$ | | $\frac{6}{9}$

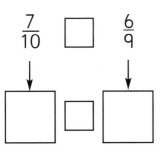

8. $\frac{3}{8}$ | | $\frac{3}{7}$

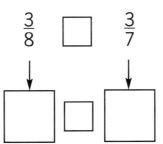

9. $\frac{6}{10}$ | | $\frac{4}{7}$

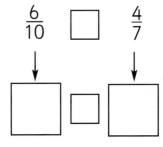

10 $\frac{8}{9}$ | | $\frac{6}{7}$

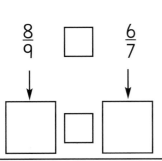

11. $\frac{8}{10}$ | | $\frac{6}{8}$

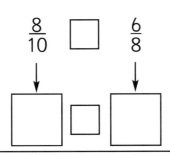

12. $\frac{2}{9}$ | | $\frac{3}{10}$

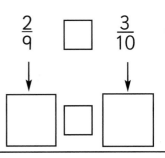

Now try this!

- Write the fractions on the apples in order, using a | common denominator |. Start with the smallest.

 $\frac{1}{5}$ $\frac{9}{10}$ $\frac{1}{2}$ $\frac{5}{6}$ $\frac{3}{10}$

Teachers' note Revise the use of the 'greater than' and 'less than' signs before the children complete this activity. Encourage the children to list multiples of each denominator to find a common one, preferably the lowest.

Developing Numeracy
Numbers and the Number System
Year 6
© A & C Black 2000

Fraction lines

• **Join each fraction to the correct position on the number line.**

1. 0 ──────────────────────────── 1

| $\dfrac{1}{2}$ | $\dfrac{1}{30}$ | $\dfrac{3}{10}$ | $\dfrac{18}{30}$ | $\dfrac{21}{30}$ | $\dfrac{8}{10}$ | $\dfrac{9}{10}$ |

2. 0 ──────────────────────────── 1

| $\dfrac{4}{30}$ | $\dfrac{6}{15}$ | $\dfrac{5}{10}$ | $\dfrac{3}{5}$ | $\dfrac{2}{3}$ | $\dfrac{5}{6}$ | $\dfrac{29}{30}$ |

• **Write the fractions that are shown on the number line.**

3. 0 ──────────────────────────── 1

$\dfrac{1}{1}$ $\dfrac{1}{ }$ $\dfrac{2}{2}$ $\dfrac{}{2}$ $\dfrac{5}{ }$ $\dfrac{}{9}$

4. 2 ──────────── 3 ──────────── 4

• **Complete these statements using $\boxed{>}$ or $\boxed{<}$.**

1. $\dfrac{7}{10}$ $\square$ $\dfrac{4}{5}$ **2.** $\dfrac{14}{30}$ $\square$ $\dfrac{6}{15}$

3. $\dfrac{5}{15}$ $\square$ $\dfrac{11}{30}$ **4.** $\dfrac{9}{15}$ $\square$ $\dfrac{2}{5}$

Teachers' note Before the children tackle this sheet, revise work on common denominators to enable the children to convert to equivalent fractions where necessary.

**Developing Numeracy
Numbers and the Number Sys**
Year 6
© A & C Black 2000

Division match

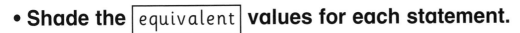

- **Shade the** | equivalent | **values for each statement.**

1.
$52 \div 10$
$52 \div 5$
£52 shared between five people
$\frac{58}{6}$
$\frac{52}{10}$
$10\frac{2}{5}$
$58 \div 6$
$\frac{52}{5}$

2.
$57 \div 10$
$11\frac{2}{5}$
£57 shared between five people
$10\frac{2}{5}$
$\frac{57}{5}$
$57 \div 5$
$10\frac{4}{5}$

3.
$\frac{6}{55}$
$9\frac{2}{6}$
£55 shared between six people
$\frac{55}{5}$
$55 \div 6$
$9\frac{1}{6}$
$\frac{55}{6}$

4.
$9\frac{1}{2}$
$58 \div 6$
£58 shared between six people
$\frac{6}{58}$
$\frac{58}{6}$
$58 \div 7$
$9\frac{4}{6}$

5.
$59 \div 8$
$58 \div 9$
£59 shared between eight people
$\frac{8}{59}$
$7\frac{3}{8}$
$\frac{59}{8}$
$\frac{58}{9}$

6.
$8\frac{3}{7}$
$59 \div 7$
£59 shared between seven people
$7 \div 59$
$10\frac{3}{7}$
$\frac{59}{7}$

7.
$58 \div 8$
$\frac{58}{7}$
$58 \div 7$
£58 shared between seven people
$8\frac{2}{7}$
$8\frac{7}{2}$
$\frac{7}{58}$
$58 \div 6$

8.
$8 \div 55$
$6\frac{7}{8}$
$\frac{8}{55}$
£55 shared between eight people
$\frac{55}{8}$
$5\frac{7}{8}$
$55 \div 8$
$6\frac{8}{7}$

Now try this!

- **Write each division question as an** | improper fraction | **, then as a** | mixed number | **.**

Example: $47 \div 6 = \dfrac{47}{6} = 7\dfrac{5}{6}$

1. $27 \div 5 = \quad\quad =$

2. $37 \div 6 = \quad\quad =$

3. $49 \div 8 = \quad\quad =$

4. $74 \div 9 = \quad\quad =$

Teachers' note It is important for the children to be able to represent and interpret statements given in a variety of forms.

Developing Numeracy
Numbers and the Number System
Year 6
© A & C Black 2000

Fraction reaction

• **Read the question on the bug's head and fill in the missing numbers.**

1.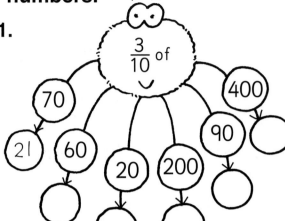

$\frac{3}{10}$ of

70 21 60 20 200 90 400

2.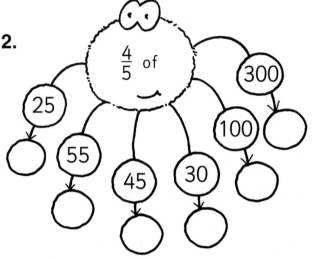

$\frac{4}{5}$ of

25 55 45 30 300 100

3.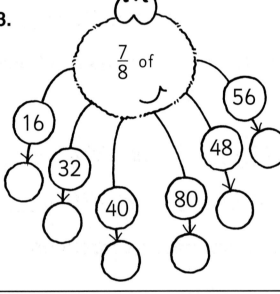

$\frac{7}{8}$ of

16 32 40 80 48 56

4.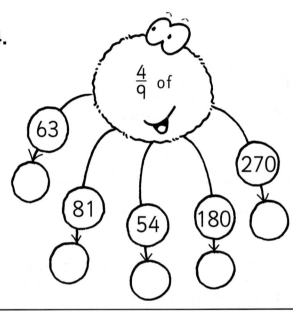

$\frac{4}{9}$ of

63 81 54 180 270

• **Fill in the missing quantities.**

Now try this!

1. $\frac{3}{100}$ of 1 m = 3 cm

2. 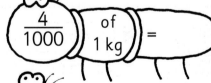 $\frac{4}{10}$ of 1 m =

3. $\frac{7}{100}$ of 1 m =

4. 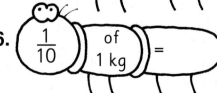 $\frac{4}{1000}$ of 1 kg =

5. 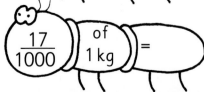 $\frac{17}{1000}$ of 1 kg =

6. $\frac{1}{10}$ of 1 kg =

Teachers' note Remind the children to divide by the denominator and multiply by the numerator to solve these questions.

Developing Numeracy
Numbers and the Number Sys
Year 6
© A & C Black 2000

Fractions of quantities

- **If** one pound **is the whole, find these amounts as fractions or mixed numbers.**

  1. 3p $\frac{3}{100}$ **2.** 17p ____ **3.** 30p ____ **4.** 50p ____

  5. £1.50 ____ **6.** £1.20 ____ **7.** £2.05 ____ **8.** £3.19 ____

- **If** one metre **is the whole, find these lengths as fractions or mixed numbers.**

  9. 4 cm $\frac{4}{100}$ **10.** 12 cm ____ **11.** 90 cm ____ **12.** 25 cm ____

  13. 1 m 99 cm ____ **14.** 4 m 30 cm ____ **15.** 6 m 12 cm ____

- **If** one kilogram **is the whole, find these weights as fractions or mixed numbers.**

  16. 1 g $\frac{1}{1000}$ **17.** 19 g ____ **18.** 47 g ____ **19.** 129 g ____

  20. 543 g ____ **21.** 798 g ____ **22.** 1822 g ____ **23.** 4761 g ____

- **If** one litre **is the whole, find these amounts as fractions or mixed numbers.**

  24. 1 ml $\frac{1}{1000}$ **25.** 49 ml ____ **26.** 225 ml ____

  27. 999 ml ____ **28.** 1284 ml ____ **29.** 3562 ml ____

- **If** a normal year **is the whole, what fraction is...**
  1. a month? _____
  2. a week? _____
  3. a day? _____

Teachers' note Remind the children of the relationship between metric units, such as grams and kilograms; litres and millilitres; centimetres and metres. Discuss the two possible fractions for one week.

Developing Numeracy
Numbers and the Number System
Year 6
© A & C Black 2000

Proportion necklaces

• Fill in the missing numbers.

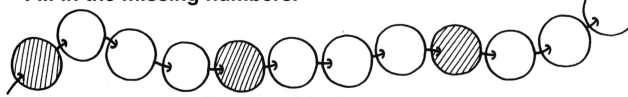

1. __1__ in every __4__ beads is black.
2. ___ in every ___ beads are white.
3. There is __ black bead to every __ white beads.
4. There are __ white beads to every __ black bead.

5. ___ in every __ beads are black.
6. ___ in every __ beads are white.
7. There are __ black beads to every __ white beads.
8. There are __ white beads to every __ black beads.

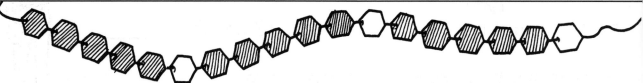

9. ___ in every __ beads are black.
10. ___ in every __ beads is white.
11. There are __ black beads to every __ white bead.
12. There is __ white bead to every __ black beads.

• Colour the necklace to match this description:

3 in every 7 beads are red;
2 in every 7 beads are white;
2 in every 7 beads are yellow;
there are 3 red beads to every 2 white beads.

Teachers' note Revise with the children the difference between 'in every' and 'to every' or 'for every' before they tackle this activity.

Developing Numeracy
Numbers and the Number Sy
Year 6
© A & C Black 2000

At the sports club

At a gym there is ☐1☐ boy for every ☐4☐ girls.

- **How many girls are there if there are**

1. 10 children? _____   **2.** 30 children? _____

3. 6 boys? _____   **4.** 8 boys? _____

- **How many boys are there if there are**

5. 15 children? _____   **6.** 25 children? _____

7. 8 girls? _____   **8.** 24 girls? _____

At the swimming club there are ☐3☐ boys for every ☐4☐ girls.

- **How many girls are there if there are**

9. 14 children? _____   **10.** 28 children? _____

11. 21 boys? _____   **12.** 42 boys? _____

- **How many boys are there if there are**

13. 42 children? _____   **14.** 49 children? _____

15. 12 girls? _____   **16.** 32 girls? _____

There are ☐30☐ children in a tennis club.
- **How many boys are there if there are**

    1. 2 girls for every boy? _____

    2. 4 girls for every boy? _____

    3. 5 girls for every boy? _____

    4. 9 boys for every girl? _____

    5. 2 boys for every 13 girls? _____

   **6.** 2 girls for every 3 boys? _____

Teachers' note Encourage the children to draw pictures of these situations if they find them difficult to visualise mentally.

Developing Numeracy
Numbers and the Number System
Year 6
© A & C Black 2000

Decimal doughnuts

- Draw lines to show which numbers can be added together to make the number in the doughnut hole.

1.
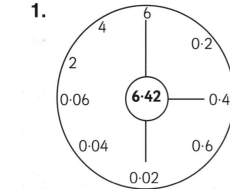

2.
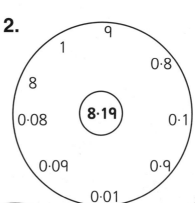

3.
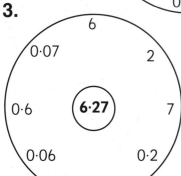

4.
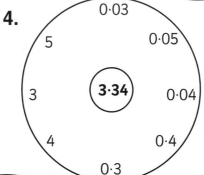

5.
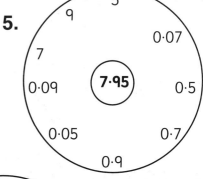

6.
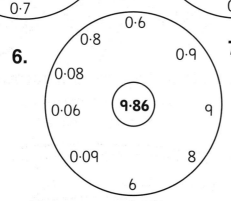

7.
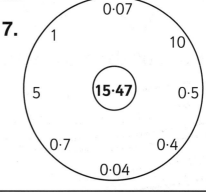

- **Which decimals are made by adding these numbers?**

1. 0·06, 10, 0·7, 5 | 15·76 | **2.** 30, 0·4, 7, 0·02 [ ]

3. 3, 0·01, 30, 0·7 [ ]   **4.** 20, 0·01, 6, 0·4 [ ]

5. 90, 0·08, 0·9 [ ]   **6.** 100, 0·06 [ ]

7. 8, 0·02, 0·7 [ ]   **8.** 0·06, 1 [ ]

9. 0·05, 0·9 [ ]   **10.** 30, 0·03 [ ]

Teachers' note The children could use a calculator to check their answers.

Developing Numeracy
Numbers and the Number Sy
Year 6
© A & C Black 2000

48

Fly the flag

- **Colour the flag that shows the value of the underlined digit.**

1. 6·2<u>7</u>4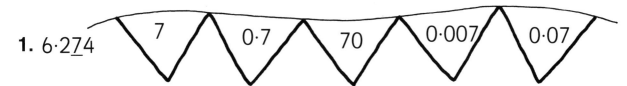
7   0·7   70   0·007   0·07

2. 8·<u>4</u>25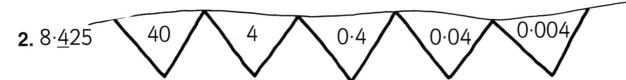
40   4   0·4   0·04   0·004

3. <u>1</u>8·361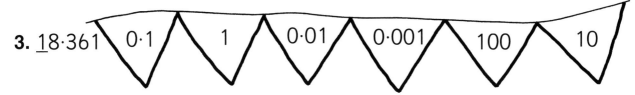
0·1   1   0·01   0·001   100   10

4. 7·14<u>6</u>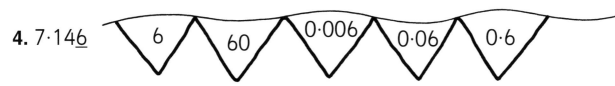
6   60   0·006   0·06   0·6

5. 100·<u>8</u>19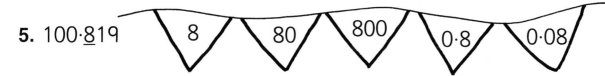
8   80   800   0·8   0·08

- **Write the total of the numbers in the flag as a decimal.**

6. six, three tenths, two hundredths, one thousandth _____

7. ninety, eight tenths, two thousandths _____

8. twelve, five hundredths, seven thousandths _____

9. one hundred, six thousandths _____

Now try this!

- **Write the value of the underlined digit as a fraction.**

1. 4·7<u>6</u>5 _____   **2.** 12·37<u>2</u> _____

3. 14·<u>1</u>090 _____   **4.** 99·999<u>9</u> _____

Teachers' note The children could write the place value column headings above the numbers to help them work out the value of the underlined digit.

Developing Numeracy
Numbers and the Number System
Year 6
© A & C Black 2000

Frog princes

- **Add or subtract a decimal to change the number on the frog into the number on the prince.**

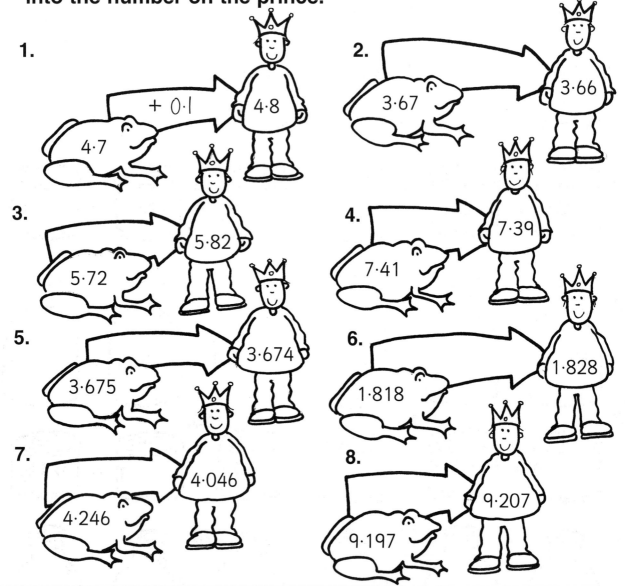

1. $4\cdot7$ $+\ 0\cdot1$ $\rightarrow$ $4\cdot8$

2. $3\cdot67$ $\rightarrow$ $3\cdot66$

3. $5\cdot72$ $\rightarrow$ $5\cdot82$

4. $7\cdot41$ $\rightarrow$ $7\cdot39$

5. $3\cdot675$ $\rightarrow$ $3\cdot674$

6. $1\cdot818$ $\rightarrow$ $1\cdot828$

7. $4\cdot246$ $\rightarrow$ $4\cdot046$

8. $9\cdot197$ $\rightarrow$ $9\cdot207$

Now try this!

- **Multiply or divide the number on the frog to change it into the number on the prince.**

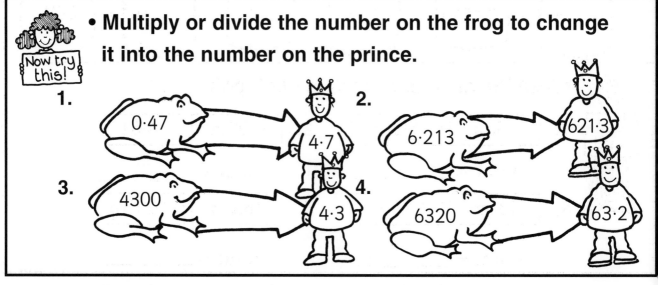

1. $0\cdot47$ $\rightarrow$ $4\cdot7$

2. $6\cdot213$ $\rightarrow$ $621\cdot3$

3. 4300 $\rightarrow$ $4\cdot3$

4. 6320 $\rightarrow$ $63\cdot2$

Teachers' note The children could use a calculator to check their answers.

Developing Numeracy
Numbers and the Number Sys
Year 6
© A & C Black 2000

Measurement madness

- **Write these measurements in metres.**

1. 25 cm = _____ m **2.** 49 cm = _____ m **3.** 186 cm = _____ m

4. 30 cm = _____ m **5.** 90 cm = _____ m **6.** 4 cm = _____ m

- **Fill in the equivalent measurements.**

7.  125 g = 0·125 kg

8.  440 g = _____ kg

9. 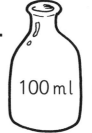 300 g = _____ kg

10. 625 ml = _____ l

11. 220 ml = _____ l

12. 100 ml = _____ l

13. _____ g = 1·615 kg

14. _____ g = 5·52 kg

15. _____ g = 0·4 kg

16. _____ ml = 0·182 l

17. _____ ml = 6·45 l

18. _____ ml = 6·2 l

 **Add the measurements in each pair.**

1. | 750 g | 1·2 kg |

total = _____

2. | 1200 ml | 4·6 l |

total = _____

3. | 13 cm | 1·47 m |

total = _____

4. | 1683 g | 1·21 kg |

total = _____

Teachers' note Remind the children of the relationships between metric units, such as grams and kilograms; litres and millilitres; centimetres and metres.

Developing Numeracy
Numbers and the Number System
Year 6
© A & C Black 2000

Dealing with decimals

- **Cut out the cards.**
- **Pick two cards and say which decimal is larger.**
     Example: $0.75 < 0.8$
- **Continue until you have used all the cards.**
- **Choose ten cards and put them in order, starting with the largest number.**

0·75	0·8	0·78	0·81
0·83	0·7	7·3	7·83
7·31	7·8	7·75	7·5
8·75	8·8	0·88	0·87
8·08	0·07	0·08	7·05
7·03	7·35	8·35	8·05

Teachers' note These cards can be used for further activities, for example, the children could each take a card and write the decimal in words (8.08 = 8 ones and 8 hundredths). Alternatively, they could find the total of two cards. This activity could be completed without cutting out the cards, by selecting adjacent numbers.

**Developing Numeracy
Numbers and the Number Sy**
Year 6
© A & C Black 2000

In the right order

• **Write these decimals in order, starting with the smallest.**

1. 6·36, 16·4, 6·89, 6·98, 6·2

6·2   6·36

2. 1·7, 1·575, 1·6, 1·65, 1·625

3. 8·875, 8·785, 8·865, 7·867, 7·886

4. 4·16, 4·67, 4·76, 4·0, 14·2

5. 5·6, 5·5, 5·66, 5·57, 5·575

Now try this!

• **Write a decimal that lies between the numbers in each pair.**

1. 6·2 [6·28] 6·3   **2.** 1·43 [ ] 1·4   **3.** 0·6 [ ] 0·7

4. 6·27 [ ] 6·28   **5.** 9·55 [ ] 9·56   **6.** 5·14 [ ] 5·13

Teachers' note Children sometimes think that if a number has three decimal places, it is automatically larger than a number with two decimal places. Explain to them that this is not necessarily the case, for example, 6.328 is not larger than 6.33.

Developing Numeracy
Numbers and the Number System
Year 6
© A & C Black 2000

Down the steps

- **Put these measurements in order. Start with the largest.**

1. 7·75 m, 17·5 m, ~~17·78 m~~

~~17·78 m~~, 7·7 m,

7·557 m

2. 0·8 kg, 1·8 kg,

1·08 kg, 1·81 kg,

1·008 kg, 10·8 kg

3. 6·222 l, 6·02 l,

6·2 l, 6·6 l,

6·22 l, 0·6 l

4. 9·4 kg, 9·99 kg,

9·099 kg, 9·9 kg,

9·09 kg, 90·9 kg

5. 12·7 l, 1·27 l,

0·127 l, 1·027 l,

2·7 l, 1·2 l

- **Use the numbers on these cards to make seven decimals.**

| 3 | 0 | . | 4 | 6 |

- **Write the decimals in order, starting with the largest.**

Teachers' note Children sometimes think that if a number has three decimal places it is automatically larger than a number with two decimal places. Explain to them that this is not necessarily the case, for example, 6.328 is not larger than 6.33.

**Developing Numeracy
Numbers and the Number S
Year 6
© A & C Black 2000**

A round of decimals

• Round the decimals to complete the chart.

	decimal	rounded to the nearest whole number	rounded to the nearest tenth
1.	6·62	7	6·6
2.	8·49		
3.	7·31		
4.	5·82		
5.	14·76		
6.	22·39		
7.	127·61		
8.	636·19		
9.	522·157		
10.	368·519		
11.	891·555		
12.	424·9632		
13.	329·9541		

• Round these numbers to one decimal place.

14. | 6·26 | 6·3 |

15. | 8·13 | |

16. | 7·51 | |

17. | 6·48 | |

18. | 0·99 | |

19. | 5·95 | |

• Write five decimals that round to the boxed number when they are rounded to the nearest tenth.

1. | 8·6 | 8·59   8·62 ___ ___ ___

2. | 7·9 | ___ ___ ___ ___ ___

3. | 2·0 | ___ ___ ___ ___ ___

4. | 3·1 | ___ ___ ___ ___ ___

Teachers' note Remind the children that the digit 5 is normally rounded up to the nearest ten.

Developing Numeracy
Numbers and the Number System
Year 6
© A & C Black 2000

A right pair

- **Join the** equivalent **fractions and decimals.**

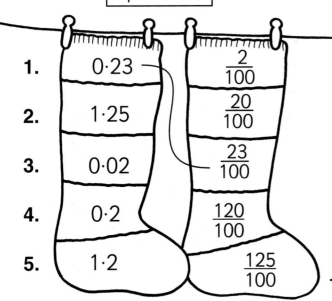

1. 0·23	$\frac{2}{100}$	**6.** 6·2	$\frac{602}{100}$
2. 1·25	$\frac{20}{100}$	**7.** 0·62	$\frac{66}{100}$
3. 0·02	$\frac{23}{100}$	**8.** 6·02	$\frac{62}{100}$
4. 0·2	$\frac{120}{100}$	**9.** 6·6	$\frac{620}{100}$
5. 1·2	$\frac{125}{100}$	**10.** 0·66	$\frac{660}{100}$

- **Write these decimals as fractions.**

11. $0·63 = \frac{63}{100}$ **12.** $0·03 =$ ___   **13.** $1·5 =$ ___   **14.** $4·27 =$ ___

15. $0·111 =$ ___   **16.** $0·723 =$ ___   **17.** $0·616 =$ ___   **18.** $1·472 =$ ___

- **Write these fractions as decimals.**

19. $\frac{42}{100} =$ ___   **20.** $\frac{87}{100} =$ ___   **21.** $\frac{4}{100} =$ ___   **22.** $\frac{120}{100} =$ ___

Now try this!

- **Circle the fractions that are equivalent to** 1·5 **.**

$$1\frac{5}{2} \qquad \frac{150}{100} \qquad 1\frac{1}{2} \qquad 1\frac{5}{10} \qquad \frac{15}{10} \qquad \frac{15}{100}$$

- **Write three fractions that are equivalent to each of these decimals.**

1. $2·4 = 2\frac{4}{10} =$ ___ $=$ ___   **2.** $3·8 =$ ___ $=$ ___ $=$ ___

3. $1·25 =$ ___ $=$ ___ $=$ ___   **4.** $4·75 =$ ___ $=$ ___ $=$ ___

Teachers' note Remind the children that fractions and decimals are different ways of saying and writing the same thing, for example, 7/10 can also be written as 0.7.

Developing Numeracy
Numbers and the Number Sy
Year 6
© A & C Black 2000

Calculator conversions

• **Change these fractions to decimals using the** $\div$ **key on your calculator.**

Example: $\boxed{\dfrac{1}{4}} = 1 \boxed{\div} 4 = \left(0{\cdot}25\right)$

1. $\boxed{\dfrac{1}{8}} = \bigcirc$ 2. $\boxed{\dfrac{1}{3}} = \bigcirc$

3. $\boxed{\dfrac{3}{8}} = \bigcirc$ 4. $\boxed{\dfrac{2}{3}} = \bigcirc$

5. $\boxed{\dfrac{3}{4}} = \bigcirc$ 6. $\boxed{\dfrac{1}{9}} = \bigcirc$

7. $\boxed{\dfrac{4}{5}} = \bigcirc$ 8. $\boxed{\dfrac{2}{9}} = \bigcirc$

9. $\boxed{\dfrac{7}{8}} = \bigcirc$ 10. $\boxed{\dfrac{5}{9}} = \bigcirc$

11. $\boxed{\dfrac{7}{20}} = \bigcirc$ 12. $\boxed{\dfrac{7}{9}} = \bigcirc$

• **Write** $\boxed{<}$ **or** $\boxed{>}$ **to make a true statement.**

• **Check your answers on a calculator.**

13. $\dfrac{9}{20} \ \square \ \dfrac{7}{15}$ 14. $\dfrac{17}{40} \ \square \ \dfrac{11}{25}$ 15. $\dfrac{3}{8} \ \square \ \dfrac{1}{5}$

16. $\dfrac{11}{14} \ \square \ \dfrac{12}{15}$ 17. $\dfrac{50}{80} \ \square \ \dfrac{9}{15}$ 18. $\dfrac{4}{5} \ \square \ \dfrac{11}{15}$

• **Write the decimal equivalents for each fraction.**

1. $\dfrac{1}{3} =$ _____   2. $\dfrac{2}{3} =$ _____

3. $1\dfrac{1}{3}$ or $\dfrac{4}{3} =$ _____   4. $1\dfrac{2}{3}$ or $\dfrac{5}{3} =$ _____

• **What do you notice?** _____

_____

Teachers' note Discuss recurring decimals with the children in the first part of the lesson.

Developing Numeracy
Numbers and the Number System
Year 6
© A & C Black 2000

Conversion game

- **With a partner, take turns to choose a fraction from the grid and say its decimal equivalent.**
- **Your partner checks on a calculator.**
- **If you are right, put a counter on the square.**
- **The winner is the first player to have four counters in a line, horizontally, vertically or diagonally.**

$\frac{2}{4}$	$\frac{7}{100}$	$\frac{9}{10}$	$\frac{2}{10}$	$\frac{1}{3}$	$\frac{1}{4}$
$\frac{2}{8}$	$\frac{2}{5}$	$\frac{27}{50}$	$\frac{12}{25}$	$\frac{1}{8}$	$\frac{19}{50}$
$\frac{41}{50}$	$\frac{3}{15}$	$\frac{10}{30}$	$\frac{1}{5}$	$\frac{7}{10}$	$\frac{4}{5}$
$\frac{3}{4}$	$\frac{1}{10}$	$\frac{2}{3}$	$\frac{9}{1000}$	$\frac{1}{100}$	$\frac{33}{50}$
$\frac{9}{50}$	$\frac{3}{5}$	$\frac{17}{25}$	$\frac{10}{80}$	$\frac{4}{8}$	$\frac{2}{1000}$
$\frac{6}{8}$	$\frac{23}{25}$	$\frac{3}{100}$	$\frac{15}{50}$	$\frac{27}{100}$	$\frac{5}{1000}$
$\frac{1}{1000}$	$\frac{20}{30}$	$\frac{15}{1000}$	$\frac{7}{1000}$	$\frac{127}{1000}$	$\frac{8}{10}$

Teachers' note The players will need counters in two colours and a calculator. Remind the children that fractions can be converted to decimals using the ÷ key on a calculator. The children could write five of their own fractions for a friend to convert to decimals (they must know the answers themselves first).

Developing Numeracy
Numbers and the Number Syst
Year 6
© A & C Black 2000

58

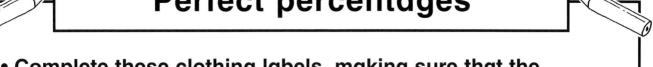

Perfect percentages

• **Complete these clothing labels, making sure that the percentages total** 100% .

1.
27% cotton
16% wool
57% silk

2.
14% viscose
39% wool
____ nylon

3.
36% silk
____ cotton
39% lycra

4.
26% nylon
18% cotton
____ lycra
15% wool

5.
13% silk
25% nylon
____ cotton
42% lycra

6.
76% viscose
8% silk
____ lycra

7.
49% cotton
37% silk
____ viscose

8.
37% lycra
37% nylon
11% cotton
____ silk

• **There are** 100 seats **in a cinema. Write the number and percentage of empty seats when:**

1. 28 seats are taken   ____ seats are empty
                              ____ % seats are empty

2. 49 seats are taken   ____ seats are empty
                              ____ % seats are empty

3. 12 seats are taken   ____ seats are empty
                              ____ % seats are empty

Now try this!

In a cinema with 200 **seats,** 42 **seats are taken.**

• **What percentage of seats**

   1. are taken? _____%

   2. are empty? _____%

Teachers' note Remind the children that in these cases all percentages must total 100.

Developing Numeracy
Numbers and the Number System
Year 6
© A & C Black 2000

Everything equivalent

• Join the ▢ equivalent ▢ fractions, percentages and decimals.

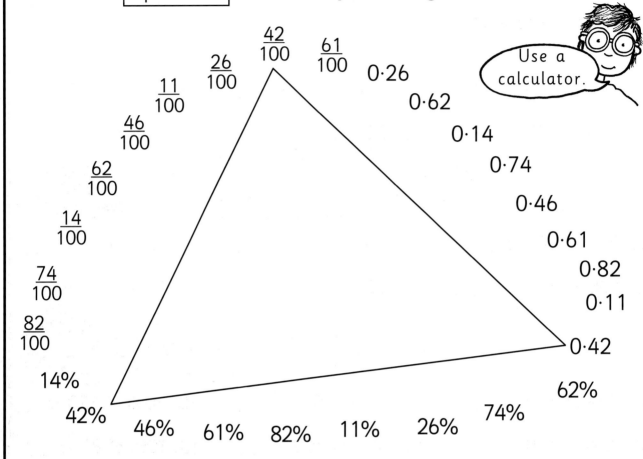

• Write each percentage as a fraction, then as a decimal.

1. 60% = $\frac{60}{100}$ = 0·6   **2.** 34% =   =

3. 92% =   =   **4.** 6% =   =

5. 30% =   =   **6.** 5% =   =

• Reduce the fractions to their simplest form.

1. $\frac{60}{100}$ = $\frac{6}{10}$ = $\frac{3}{5}$ **2.** $\frac{92}{100}$ =   =

3. $\frac{58}{100}$ =   =   **4.** $\frac{34}{100}$ =   =

5. $\frac{4}{100}$ =   =   **6.** $\frac{5}{100}$ =   =

Teachers' note Remind the children that the percentage sign can be thought of as 'out of 100'.

Developing Numeracy
Numbers and the Number Sys
Year 6
© A & C Black

Find the percentage

- **Calculate the answer to each question.**

> To find 25%, halve the number and halve it again.

1. 25% of 600 is _150_

2. 25% of 300 is ___

3. 25% of 400 is ___

4. 25% of 380 is ___

5. 25% of 260 is ___

6. 25% of 540 is ___

> To find 75%, find 25% and take it away from the original number.

7. 75% of 600 is ___

8. 75% of 300 is ___

9. 75% of 400 is ___

10. 75% of 380 is ___

11. 75% of 260 is ___

12. 75% of 540 is ___

> To find 10%, divide by 10.

13. 10% of 30 is ___

14. 10% of 900 is ___

15. 10% of 120 is ___

16. 10% of 110 is ___

17. 10% of 700 is ___

18. 10% of 80 is ___

> Use your answers for 10% to help you find 80%.

19. 80% of 30 is ___

20. 80% of 900 is ___

21. 80% of 120 is ___

22. 80% of 110 is ___

23. 80% of 700 is ___

24. 80% of 80 is ___

> To find 90%, work out 10% first!

25. 90% of 60 is ___

26. 90% of 80 is ___

27. 90% of 300 is ___

28. 90% of 900 is ___

29. 90% of 400 is ___

30. 90% of 110 is ___

- **Write a rule for finding** 40% **of a number.**
- **Use the rule to find** 40% **of all the multiples of ten between** 49 **and** 99 .

Teachers' note Once the children appreciate that 10% is one tenth, they can be shown that 20%, 30%, 40% are two tenths, three tenths, four tenths, and so on.

Developing Numeracy
Numbers and the Number System
Year 6
© A & C Black 2000

Percentage path

- **Work in pairs.**
- **Follow the path and calculate each percentage.**

start

25% of £300 is _____

30% of £8 is _____

60% of 20 m is _____

70% of 40 kg is _____

50% of 18 l is _____

3 0 4 2 5 7

40% of 120 kg is _____

70% of 200 m is _____

50% of 3·6 cm is _____

20% of 30 kg is _____

90% of £60 is _____

10% of 130 cm is _____

75% of £400 is _____

5% of 80 m is _____

1% of £500 is _____

30% of £30 is _____

25% of 80 km is _____

75% of 48 m is _____

25% of 9·2 g is _____

50% of 14·28 l is _____

80% of 70 m is _____

90% of 180 kg is _____

40% of 30 m is _____

2% of 50 kg is _____

25% of 18 l is _____

$12\frac{1}{2}$% of 8 l is _____

finish

Now try this!

- **Find the prices of six items in a catalogue.**
- **Calculate what the new prices would be if there was** 10% off **in a sale.**

Teachers' note Encourage children to try these mentally first. For example, to work out 25% they need to halve the number and halve it again.

Developing Numeracy
Numbers and the Number Sy
Year 6
© A & C Black 200

Sale time

Shop One is selling everything at 80% **of the old price.**

• **Write the sale price for each item.**

1. computer game

£120 sale price

2. trainers

£68 sale price

3. tennis racket

£47 sale price

4. football kit

£25 sale price

5. football

£12.50 sale price

6. cap

£4.25 sale price

Shop Two is selling everything at 75% **of the old price.**

• **Write the sale price for each item.**

7. computer game

£130 sale price

8. trainers

£70 sale price

9. tennis racket

£50 sale price

10. football kit

£26 sale price

11. football

£13.40 sale price

12. cap

£5.80 sale price

Now try this!

• **Complete the table to show which shop sells the item more cheaply.**

	computer game	trainers	tennis racket	football kit	football	cap
Shop One	✓					
Shop Two						

Teachers' note Encourage the children to estimate the new price before working it out on a calculator.

Developing Numeracy
Numbers and the Number System
Year 6
© A & C Black 2000

Testing times

Here are some children's test scores.

- **Work out the percentage for each child.**
- **If necessary, round the percentage to the nearest whole number.**

Use a calculator.

1.  $\frac{12}{16}$ = _75_ %

2.  $\frac{13}{25}$ = ___ %

3. $\frac{38}{50}$ = ___ %

4.  $\frac{24}{40}$ = ___ %

5.  $\frac{46}{80}$ = ___ %

6. 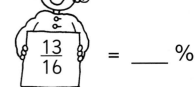 $\frac{13}{16}$ = ___ %

7.  $\frac{27}{32}$ = ___ %

8.  $\frac{45}{65}$ = ___ %

9.  $\frac{48}{90}$ = ___ %

10.  $\frac{37}{64}$ = ___ %

11.  $\frac{64}{70}$ = ___ %

12. 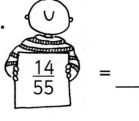 $\frac{14}{55}$ = ___ %

Now try this!

- **Write the children's test scores as fractions in order, starting with the lowest.**

 $\frac{14}{55}$ ◯ ◯ ◯ ◯ ◯ ◯ ◯ ◯ ◯ ◯ ◯

Teachers' note Demonstrate to the children how to use the division key on a calculator to convert fractions to decimals and then to multiply this number by 100 to find the percentage.

**Developing Numeracy
Numbers and the Number Sy**
Year 6
© A & C Black 2000